G000272619

THE TYNE TUNNELS

"TIME ONCE LOST TO TRAFFIC JAMS CAN NOW BE SPENT WITH FAMILY AND FRIENDS"

Author: Tamsin Greulich Editorial Team: Paul Fenwick Trevor Jackson Rachel Turnbull Richard Simpson Peter Hedley Designer: Ian Guy

Major Civil Engineering Project of the Year 2012

NORTH TORIES ALLEGE 'DIRTY PLAY'

A rubber stamp sparks off election row

MERGER MAY END BUILDING PROJECT

ROBOTS WILL AID TUNNEL MOTORISTS

New flats 'will banish drudgery for housewives'

Police tell of 'The till, or I shoot' threat

Council to fight veto on housing

Warrant out for man's arrest

Their 'credit' was stolen

Petition for new windows

POLICE COULDN'T ROUSE YOUTH

THERE'S AN EXTRA 2%

5% NATIONAL DEVELOPMENT BONDS

Tyne Tunnel begins to-day

MINISTER TO START WORK

ONE of the largest civil engineering projects ever tackled on Tyneside will be initiated to-day when the Minister of Transport (Mr. A. Barnes) cuts the first sods at Wallsend and Jarrow and starts the Tyne Tunnel.

The job may take over five years to complete and absorb between £3,000,000 and £6,000,000 before "completion day."

1926 P60.

In 1926, the Ministry of Transport made a Provisional Order authorising construction of the new tunnel, but some aspects of the scheme were the subject of local objections and the House of Commons rejected the subsequent Bill on the second reading.

1920 P60.

1920s - In order to meet the growing, and widely recognised, need for a river crossing east of Newcastle, towards the sea, a proposal was considered during the 1920s for a tunnel between North and South Shields. This was to carry high-speed electric monorail cars.

1937 P60.

In 1937, the Durham and Northumberland County Councils put forward a scheme for a road tunnel under the river between Howdon and Jarrow, and after prolonged negotiation and discussion their plan was approved by the then minister of transport in 1943. Matters were delayed by the war, but as soon as hostilities ended the two Councils promoted the necessary Bill which duly received the Royal Assent as the Tyne Tunnel Act, 1946. Owing to the restrictions on capital expenditure introduced in 1947 however, the then Minister, the Right Hon. Alfred Barnes M.P., ruled that for the time being work should be confined to the pedestrian and cycle tunnels only. The work of driving these tunnels began in June 1947.

HOE'S SAUCE

WEEKLY CHRONICLE

RIVER TYNE

TYNE TUNNEL

1951 P86.

In 1951, the completed tunnels were opened by the Minister of Transport, the Right Hon. Alfred Barnes, M.P., on the 24th July 1951. The Waygood-Otis escalators were installed in the inclined vertical rise of 85 ft. They are also the first in the country to be used by cyclists as well as by pedestrians.

Queen to open Tyne Tunnel

THE QUEEN is to open the Tyne Tunnel on October 19.

She and Prince Philip will both visit the North-East on that day.

The Queen will also officially open the £1m. sports forum at Billingham.

She will be in the town for an hour, and after carrying out the official opening of the forum, it is expected she will be escorted round the now almost completed new town centre.

After her visit to Billingham

2002 P30.

2000, in order to address the increasing demands
for extra capacity at the Tyne Tunnel, the TWPTA submits an application to the Secretary of State for Transport for an Order under the Transport and Works Act to proceed with a proposal to construct an immersed tube tunnel.

1986 P28.

1986 - Tyne and Wear Passenger Transport Authority (TWPTA)
takes over responsibility for the operation of the Tyne Tunnels from the Tyne and Wear Metropolitan County Council.

In 1961 the Tyne Vehicle Tunnel
was developed under the direction of the Tyne Tunnels Joint Committee. Construction began in 1961.

A Tyne Tunnel toll?

By J. D. MARGACH,
Our Political Correspondent.

IF plans are presented from Newcastle for tolls to be levied to help meet the cost of the Tyne Tunnel scheme they will be examined carefully and sympathetically by the Government.

Mr. Alan Lennox-Boyd, Minister of Transport, has a "completely open mind about tolls," he says.

There is a case, in his opinion, for considering tolls in relation to bridges and tunnels where traffic is saved an expensive detour.

Other schemes

At present three of the major schemes in this country include provision for tolls. The Mersey Tunnel was built on a toll basis, the Dartford-Purfleet scheme allows for tolls when the tunnel is completed, and the Forth Bridge Act makes similar provision.

North-East M.P.s are expected to press the Minister to include the Tyne Tunnel project in his new programme.

At the moment the Tyne plan cannot be included in the programme for the first three years, but it is confidently believed that the Minister is anxious to have it approved as soon as possible in the subsequent programme.

Gilbert Harding

Gilbert Harding, who is in the London Clinic with acute bronchial trouble, was today stated to have had "a comfortable night" and to be "maintaining his progress."

1967 P68.

In October 1967 Her Majesty The Queen
opened the new Vehicle Tunnel, accompanied by His Royal Highness The Duke of Edinburgh.

THE JOURNAL Thursday April 13 1967

Starting to see daylight

By Journal Reporter

THE TYNE TUNNEL is in the process of being dressed up in style for its first public showing in the early autumn.

The mud and clutter that has marked the site on each side of the river for the past five years is rapidly being replaced by order and design.

Grass and shrubs have already been planted in the approaches in anticipation of the work being completed in the last week of August.

The smart "top show" fittings already installed include walls lined with Italian mosaic inside the tunnel and a sun-visor at the Howdon entrance.

HONEYCOMB

The sun-visor, 160ft. of white concrete, has been built to an open lattice-work design to ease the sudden transition from ...

20 OCT 1968 "SUNDAY SUN"

One-year-old Tyne tunnel a 'great success'

SUNDAY SUN REPORTER

THE TYNE TUNNEL, built over six years at a cost of £13m., is one-year-old today, and last night it was described by Alderman Dan Dawson, chairman of the Tyne Tunnel Joint Committee, as "a smashing success."

"If ever money was well spent this was it," he said. "I have been in on this ... from the start

2003 P30.

2003, a public inquiry
is held in spring 2003 at which all the issues of building the New Tyne Crossing are addressed and considered.

2005 P30.

2005, the Secretary of State for Transport
approves the scheme to construct the New Tyne Crossing in July 2005.
A legal challenge to the Secretary of State's decision is made by a member of the public within six weeks of the approval, delaying the appointment of a Concessionaire.

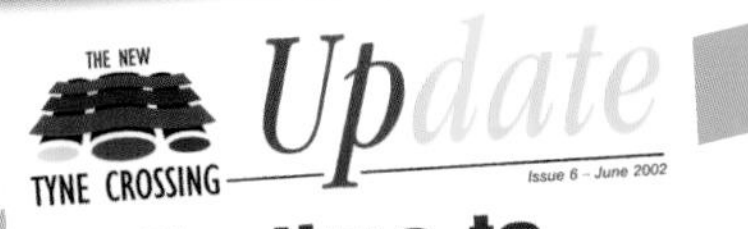

Issue 6 – June 2002

Write time to give your views

Members of the public and organisations have until 15 July to send letters of support or objection about the proposed New Tyne Crossing to the Secretary of State for Transport and the Regions.

Tyne and Wear Passenger Transport Authority (PTA), which is sponsoring the project, supported by North Tyneside and South Tyneside Councils, applied for the necessary powers to build an immersed tube tunnel between Jarrow and Howdon on 31 May.

It is expected that the Secretary of State will call a Public Inquiry for later in the year when all the issues surrounding the construction and future operation of the tunnel will be aired.

Jarrow councillor and PTA deputy vice chair Tom Hanson urged people to write.

"The PTA sees the new tunnel as vital to the whole of Tyne and Wear, but particularly to South Tyneside which has the highest levels of unemployment," he said.

"The vehicular crossings of the Tyne from Blaydon to the existing tunnel are now at capacity most of the day. The New Tyne Crossing will relieve congestion and so eliminate the delays which motorists currently endure at the Tyne Tunnel. It will also, to some extent, ease the situation on other crossings.

"The PTA is committed to keeping the public informed about the scheme. We will be holding exhibitions and making the application documents available in several locations.

PTA vice and deputy vice chairs Muriel Green and Tom Hanson deliver the application to Government Office North East

"I hope people will take the opportunity to find out about the scheme and write to the Secretary of State whether they support it or not."

The address is shown overleaf.

See exhibition venues and times on back page.

2006 P30.

2006, the legal challenge
to the New Tyne Crossing is dismissed by the High Court in spring 2006. The challenger seeks leave to appeal to the Appeal Court. This is refused in August 2006.
In the meantime, the two remaining Concessionaire bidders are invited to submit tenders. These are received in August 2006.

2007 P32.

2007, the appointment of the preferred bidder,
a Bouygues-led consortium, is made on 12 April 2007. A period of negotiation concludes with the final contract signed in November 2007. This marks the appointment of the Concessionaire (TT2 Limited) who will finance, design and build the new tunnel, and operate and maintain all the tunnels, for up to 30 years.

2008 P32.

2008. 1st February 2008
all tunnel assets and staff are transferred to TT2 Limited.
Construction of the New Tyne Crossing starts, with vegetation clearance taking place along the entire length of the construction corridor from January 2008, and site fencing and enabling works beginning in April 2008.

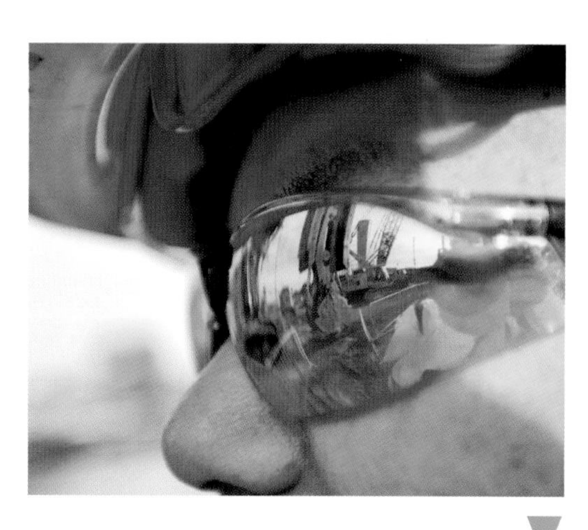

2009 P42.

November 2009. Dredging of the bed
of the River Tyne takes place during November and December. The dry dock at Walker is flooded in preparation for floating the immersed tube tunnel elements along the river, to lower into the dredged trench.

2010 P48.

January 2010. The first river tunnel
element is lowered into place in the river bed, to create the river section of the new vehicle tunnel.

July 2010, a commemorative walk
through the new vehicle tunnel takes place, marking the first opportunity to travel beneath the Tyne in the new tunnel.

2011 P58.

February 2011. The new vehicle tunnel
is commissioned for use at midnight on 25th February 2011. At the same time all Tyne Tunnel traffic is diverted into the new tunnel as the original vehicle tunnel closes. Work commences on the full refurbishment of the 1967-built tunnel. Work also starts on re-landscaping the environment which had formed the construction corridor.

November 2011. The refurbished 1967 tunnel
is returned to use, offering two road tunnels for motorists, and immediately eradicating congestion at the river crossing.

2012 P96.

Her Majesty The Queen, accompanied by His Royal Highness the Duke of Edinburgh, officially opened the new Tyne Tunnel on 18th July 2012
as part of her Diamond Jubilee Tour of the North East.

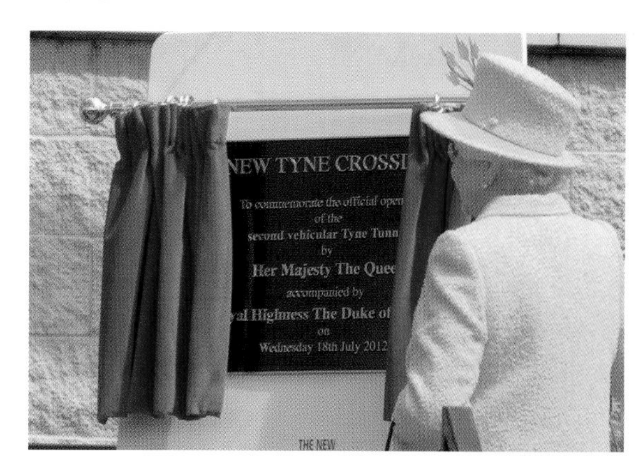

INTRO

"I remember standing at the dry dock in Walker on a freezing winter's day watching as huge concrete boxes were carefully and expertly floated into the river before beginning their journey downstream to become part of the new Tyne vehicle tunnel.

My father once worked at that dry dock. I wondered what he would have made of the four enormous structures and the 'immersed tube' technology they represented. I'm sure that, like me, he would have been amazed and awe-struck at the skill and expertise required for this part of the project.

But this 'immersed tube' section of the second tunnel was only part of the New Tyne Crossing - one of the most complex civil engineering projects ever undertaken in Tyne and Wear.

Today, watching the traffic flow freely through the tunnels is nothing short of miraculous when compared to the long queues of slow-moving traffic that not so long ago blighted this part of Tyneside. It is a vindication, if any were needed, of the decision to go ahead with the New Tyne Crossing.

That the New Tyne Crossing was achieved ahead of schedule and praised by local people for the excellent way it was managed is a tribute to everyone involved.

On behalf of the Members of the Transport Authority, I would like to take this opportunity of thanking my team and our advisers, especially our Project Director Paul Fenwick; the Concessionaire TT2 led by Trevor Jackson; and the contractor Bouygues Travaux Publics led by Nicolas Caille, for making the New Tyne Crossing the success it is. The commitment and skill of everyone involved has contributed to creating a major improvement in the transport infrastructure of Tyne & Wear which will help the area in its efforts to create jobs and prosperity over the coming years.

Finally, I would like to thank the people of Jarrow and East Howdon and surrounding area for their forbearance, understanding and patience during the construction of the new tunnel. I sincerely hope their quality of life and job opportunities are significantly enhanced as a result of the New Tyne Crossing."

Councillor David Wood, Chairman, Tyne and Wear Integrated Transport Authority

In 2009 the Tyne and Wear Passenger Transport Authority, owners of the Tyne Tunnels since 1986, were re-named as the Tyne and Wear Integrated Transport Authority (TWITA). For simplicity the Transport Authority will be referred to as TWITA throughout this book.

Rachel Turnbull, Chief Executive Officer, TT2 Limited

"I am immensely proud of what we have achieved with this project. Since I joined TT2, back in 2007, we have faced what felt like 'the impossible'.

The most significant civil engineering scheme in the North East for years was to be entirely self-funded. We brought innovation into the funding solution so that this became a reality.

We had a gridlocked site that we had to try to keep moving while complex building works snaked around it. Everyone expected traffic chaos, yet we managed to actually improve journey times for most people during the construction phase.

The route of the new tunnel cut a trench through communities, and people feared years of tough living conditions as a result. Instead, many local residents told us the works had been far easier to live with than they'd anticipated. They praised the way the works had been delivered and thanked us for keeping them involved.

The most impossible challenge we faced was removing one of the UK's worst traffic bottlenecks. Not many people believed the New Tyne Crossing would make such a difference to traffic flow. Overnight the notorious Tyne Tunnel traffic jams disappeared. With two Tyne Tunnels life for thousands of people has been transformed, and the A19 has emerged as the route of choice for millions of motorists a year.

Thanks go to the thousands of people who have worked together to deliver the award winning New Tyne Crossing project, and to the patient and supportive residents, schools, community groups, and businesses who have helped this to become the most important river crossing of the Tyne."

Nicolas Caille, Project Director, Bouygues Travaux Publics UK

"There were some unique challenges associated with this project. We had a site criss-crossed with utilities, closely bounded by homes and schools, with varying and difficult ground conditions. The bed of the River Tyne contained contaminants from previous industrial activities, whilst also being heavily populated with salmon. Furthermore, the site encompassed the fourth most congested traffic spot in the country.

The success of this project is the result of partnership working and careful planning. As an engineer I relish the challenges that come with a project of this scale and complexity, and I thoroughly enjoyed the range of issues we encountered at the Tyne Tunnels.

I'm pleased to say that by working through the unexpected obstacles we faced on the New Tyne Crossing scheme we were able to identify even better ways of doing things, for the benefit of the environment, local people, and regional development.

THIS book tells the tale of four unique crossings of the River Tyne: hidden conduits beneath a mighty river that once formed a defensive barrier between the communities along its banks. As bridges grew across the Tyne at Newcastle and Gateshead, seven miles upstream, people wishing to cross the river further east were served only by ferries. At least, that was the case until an altogether different idea for crossing the Tyne came to fruition. The journey under the river became possible when the first Tyne Tunnels were born.

Records suggest that a ferry service existed from 1850 onwards to connect the banks of the Tyne between Jarrow and Howdon / Willington Quay. Various organisations ran a service along this route over the years that it operated. In 1951, with the opening of the Tyne Pedestrian and Cyclist Tunnels, Durham and Northumberland Councils took over management of the ferry crossing to Willington Quay, which they were also responsible for. The ferry service, which accommodated vehicles, stopped completely in 1967 upon the opening of the first Tyne Vehicle Tunnel.

EADLIGHTS
TYNE TUNNELS
WORKS
EXIT
PB
TYNE TUNNELS
NOW SHOWING
THE GHOST

DURING construction of the newest tunnel, completed in February 2011, a considerable interest in the tunnels became apparent. Curious observers from around the world followed project progress online with enthusiastic dedication. Local residents filled personal scrap books with images, press cuttings, and memorabilia of a local landmark under development. Local school children created artworks depicting their view of the project taking shape on the other side of the school fence. People felt they were watching history in the making. The opening ceremonies for the first Tyne Tunnels are etched into local memory: recollections of school children waving flags; engineers' wives placing posies of flowers into the "royal WC"; new hats bought and pinned securely in place to combat the ferocious winds that hounded Her Majesty Queen Elizabeth II's visit in 1967. Construction of the new tunnel revealed that, despite the notorious traffic jams each rush hour, people delighted in sharing their tunnel stories, and wanted to know more about this infamous river crossing.

And so this book came to life. This is the first, fully illustrated story of the Tyne Tunnels, written by those at the heart of the New Tyne Crossing project, and featuring the characters who have breathed life into what is essentially steel, concrete, and four tubes in the ground.

THE SETTING

The Tyne Tunnels are located beneath the River Tyne in North East England, connecting Jarrow in South Tyneside with East Howdon in North Tyneside. The Tyne Tunnels are approximately seven miles east (downstream) of the river crossings between Newcastle and Gateshead, and three miles west (upstream) of the North Sea.

There are four tunnels at the site:
Pedestrian and Cyclist Tunnels, which are accessed from the river banks either side of the Tyne, and two Vehicle Tunnels, entered further away from the river's edge, as part of the A19 trunk road. The four tunnels run alongside each other, at different depths.

What is the New Tyne Crossing Project?

THE New Tyne Crossing is the project devised to more than double the number of vehicles that could pass through the Tyne Tunnels site every day. The original road tunnel offered a single carriageway for traffic in each direction. It was designed to accept 24,000 vehicles a day, a figure that was exceeded on a daily basis by the 1980s. By building a second road tunnel and new toll plazas, restructuring the complex junction to the south of the tunnel, and overhauling of the original road tunnel, the most significant transformation of North East traffic flow in decades was made possible through this project.

Once both tunnels were fully operational, by November 2011, the new tunnel provided a southbound dual carriageway, and the original tunnel offered two northbound lanes.

The New Tyne Crossing is the project responsible for eradicating congestion at one of the North East's most infamous traffic pinch points. Commuters using the route when the two vehicle tunnels came into operation described the effect as "transformational" and "incredible".

The benefits of the project are not simply measured by the reduction in traffic jams on the tunnel approaches. Positive impacts have been widely felt, and have meant different things to different people. From getting home early enough to put children to bed, to improved business productivity, North East commuters have been proud to proclaim "We love the Tyne Tunnels!"

TT2 contracted specialist firm Bouygues Travaux Publics UK (Bouygues TP) as the main design and build contractor for the New Tyne Crossing project. Bouygues TP had a proven track record in the design and build of immersed tube tunnels, the design chosen by TWITA for the second Tyne road tunnel. Bouygues TP also managed and delivered the refurbishment of the original road tunnel to modern design standards. They provided the expertise to lead the design and build services, predominantly using local firms to deliver the work on the ground.

Who is behind the project?

The New Tyne Crossing project is a Public Private Partnership between the Project Promoter, the Tyne and Wear Integrated Transport Authority (TWITA), and the Project Concessionaire, TT2 Limited, with the main design and build contract delivered by Bouygues Travaux Publics UK.

TWITA is the authority whose responsibility it is to manage strategic transport issues across Tyne and Wear. It is an authority made up of the five Tyne and Wear local authorities, with administrative functions delivered through Newcastle City Council. TWITA took ownership of the Tyne Tunnels site in 1986, and is the organisation responsible for proposing and promoting the concept of the New Tyne Crossing.

TWITA led the project through Public Inquiry and the subsequent tendering process to let a 30 year concession contract to deliver the £260 million project in 2007.

TT2 Limited is the project Concessionaire, and a "Special Purpose Vehicle" company whose sole purpose is to deliver the New Tyne Crossing project for TWITA. TT2 was set up to oversee the design and build of the new Vehicle Tunnel, the refurbishment of the original Vehicle Tunnel, and to operate and maintain all four Tyne Tunnels over the thirty year concession period. In February 2008 all Tyne Tunnel staff, previously employed by TWITA, were transferred into the employment of TT2.

There was a strong and genuine commitment from the three main project parties, TWITA, TT2 and Bouygues TP, to deliver the scheme together, in partnership. The dedicated efforts to jointly discuss and collaboratively seek solutions to the issues arising during construction helped the New Tyne Crossing project to be delivered smoothly and ahead of schedule, minimising impacts on road users and local communities. However, the desire to work in partnership was not restricted to the project Promoter, Concessionaire, and main Contractor. Partnerships were forged with the riparian authorities, with local communities and businesses, with emergency services, and with special interest groups to ensure that the New Tyne Crossing was a project that took its stakeholders with it on the journey, from the earliest development stages through to completion.

THE NEW TYNE TUNNEL

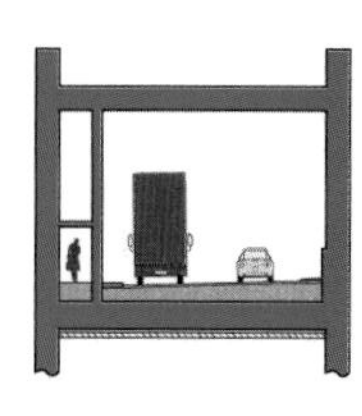

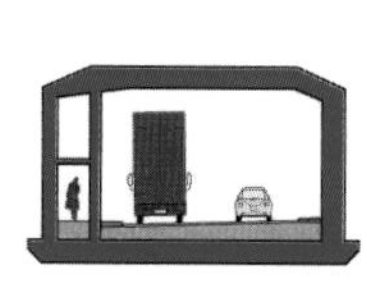

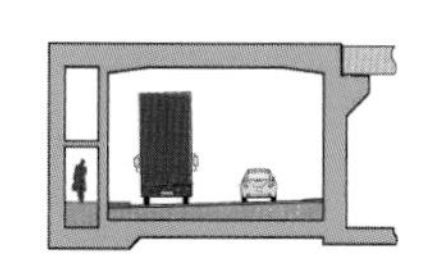

Cross sections of the new vehicle tunnel

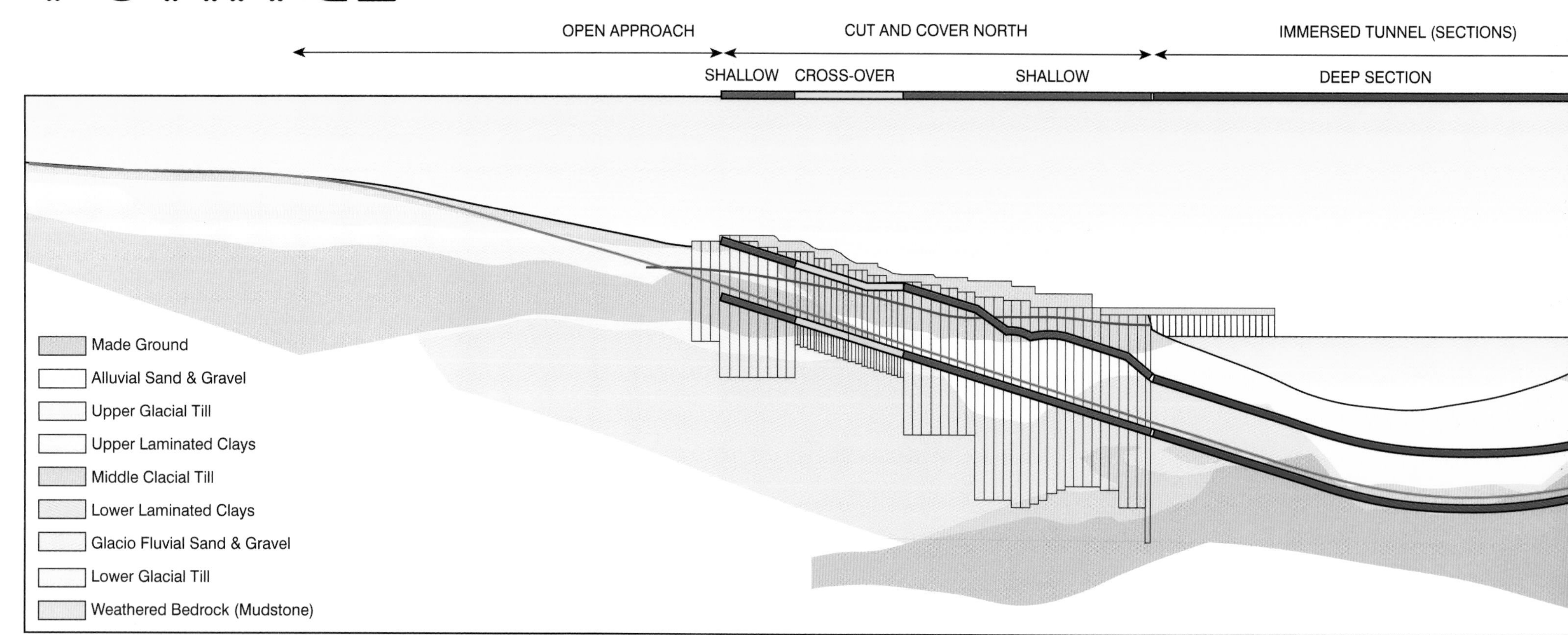

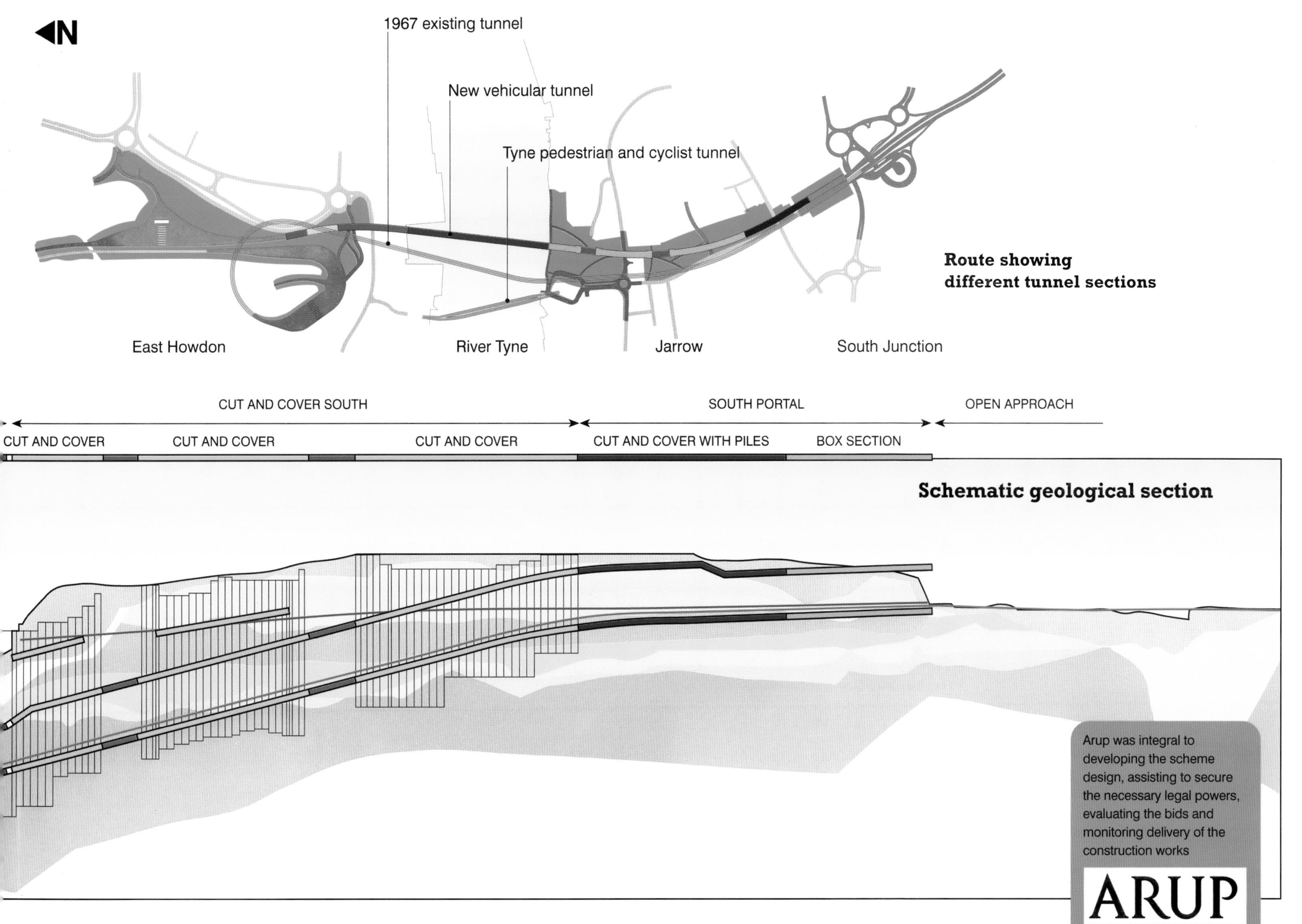
N
1967 existing tunnel
New vehicular tunnel
Tyne pedestrian and cyclist tunnel
Route showing different tunnel sections
East Howdon
River Tyne
Jarrow
South Junction
CUT AND COVER SOUTH
SOUTH PORTAL
OPEN APPROACH
CUT AND COVER
CUT AND COVER
CUT AND COVER
CUT AND COVER WITH PILES
BOX SECTION
Schematic geological section
Arup was integral to developing the scheme design, assisting to secure the necessary legal powers, evaluating the bids and monitoring delivery of the construction works
ARUP

Beneath the land: cut and cover tunnels

- Build underground tunnel walls by excavating slim trenches and filling with liquid clay to prevent collapse
- Add reinforcement and concrete to trenches to create underground 'diaphragm' walls
- Remove soil from between the underground walls and support the space with props, to create a trench
- Build tunnel from reinforced concrete at the bottom of the trench
- Refill trench with soil and landscape above

Connecting land tunnels to river tunnel: transition structure

- Build deep underground concrete boxes on each river bank in the same way as the tunnel diaphragm walls
- Excavate soil from within the underground box to create a deep narrow shaft in each river bank
- Install a seal on the inner wall of each transition structure, designed to connect to the seal at the end of the river tunnel units
- Demolish the outer (riverside) wall of the transition structure

Beneath the river: immersed tube technology

- Dredge the river bed
- Build four tunnel units in dry dock
- Float units along river and lower into trench
- Connect river units to land tunnels via the transition structures
- Remove temporary ballast tanks and bulk head walls from inside tunnel units to create a single unit

Avoiding Utilities: Sprayed Concrete Lining

- Instead of cutting a trench through existing major utilities, the area beneath would be excavated from the bottom of the tunnel trench
- The excavated space is reinforced with supports and by spraying concrete onto the excavated walls
- The space is lined with waterproofed lining
- Fireboards are installed to provide extra protection, as the concrete walls are thinner in these tunnel sections

Protecting the original tunnel: Cross Over Section

- North of the river the new tunnel passes a few metres above the original road tunnel
- To avoiding removing the load from the top of the original tunnel, and prevent movement, the new tunnel roof was built before excavating beneath it
- Diaphragm walls were installed with shorter foundations than elsewhere along the cut and cover tunnel
- The tunnel flooring was built once the excavation was complete, with walls and roof already in place
- The original tunnel was monitored for movement throughout the works

Building in Safety

- The first tunnel in the UK to feature a Fixed Fire Suppression System to minimise risks to people and damage to the tunnel
- A dedicated safety passage was built along the entire length of the tunnel
- The air pressure in the tunnel is designed to increase during an incident, to prevent smoke from entering the safety passage
- Signage indicates closest exit
- Cameras throughout the tunnel are connected to monitoring technology to automatically detect incidents

1
Excavate slim trenches along route of tunnel and pour in concrete to create underground 'diaphragm' walls
2
Dig out trench between underground 'diaphragm' walls, supporting excavated space with props to stop trench from caving in
3
Build tunnel at base of trench
10
Refill trench once tunnel is built and replant with trees, grass and shrubs

The Ten Step Plan to Building the New Tyne Tunnel

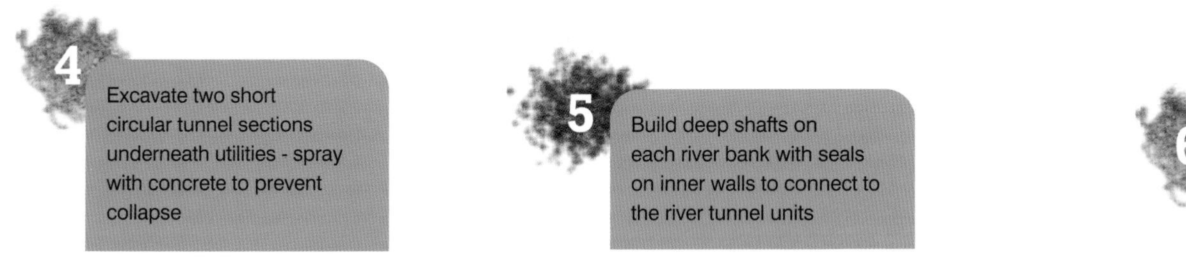

4
Excavate two short circular tunnel sections underneath utilities - spray with concrete to prevent collapse
5
Build deep shafts on each river bank with seals on inner walls to connect to the river tunnel units

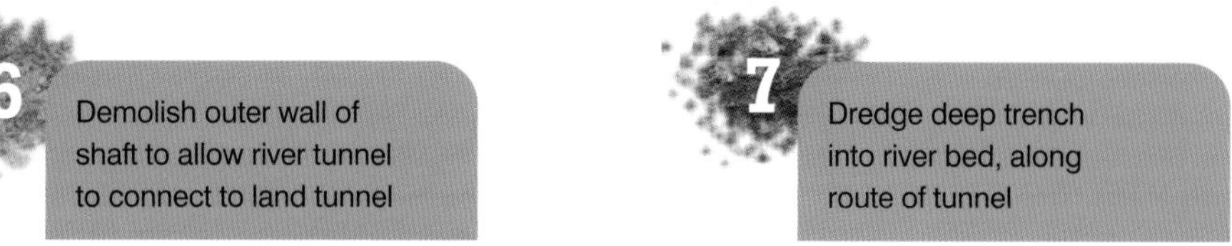

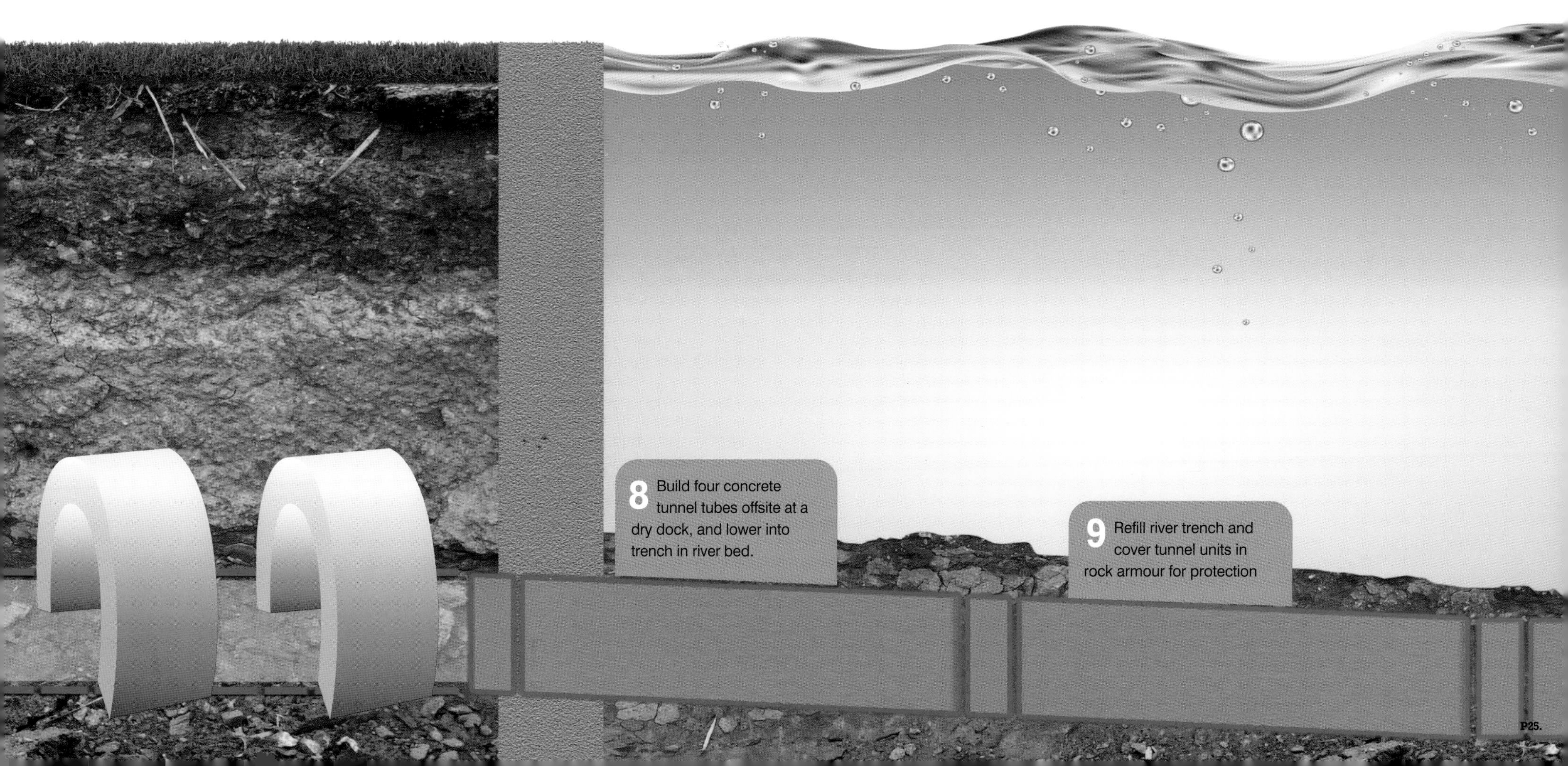

Demolish outer wall of shaft to allow river tunnel to connect to land tunnel

8
Build four concrete tunnel tubes offsite at a dry dock, and lower into trench in river bed.
9
Refill river trench and cover tunnel units in rock armour for protection

A fourth Tyne Tunnel

WHEN it opened to traffic, the second vehicular Tyne Tunnel became the first new road crossing of the River Tyne in twenty years. Delivery of this major civil engineering project had involved more than two decades of effort, from considering initial concepts, through the major planning and consultation processes, technical investigations, development of designs, and finally construction and commissioning. The construction milestones captured public interest, and were moments of great pride for the project team, but they represented only the highlights of a long journey for those involved behind the scenes.

Adams

Why build a second road tunnel?

THE original road tunnel accommodated around 4,000 vehicles a day when it first opened. It didn't take long for this smooth flowing route to get busy however. Designed to handle up to 24,000 vehicles per day, by the mid-1980s the tunnel was routinely seeing traffic numbers far higher than this. By 2007 the tunnel was carrying 50% more traffic than it was designed for, with up to 38,000 vehicles per day. It was therefore hardly surprising to see such notorious levels of congestion during peak hours.

As well as the Tyne Tunnel, the other Tyne river crossings were struggling to cope with demand. Hence the Tyneside district councils began looking at a range of models for increasing traffic capacity across the River Tyne. As well as exploring options for a new river crossing they also looked into how improvements in public transport might alleviate demand on the busy cross-Tyne routes. Studies indicated that even with substantial improvements to public transport, an additional river crossing would still be required if the pressures on the existing bridges and the original Tyne Tunnel were to be lifted.

Initial studies considered a number of river crossing options. It had been identified that extra capacity was required east of the Tyne Bridge, and eventually four crossing points were highlighted that could meet the growing traffic demands. It was left as a political decision to identify the preferred location of the new crossing out of the four options, one of which was a Tyne Bridge by-pass, two of which linked Walker across to Heworth, and the fourth was adjacent to the Tyne Tunnel. Politicians agreed that the routes through Newcastle would be more disruptive and more difficult to connect to the primary routes, and hence the proposal to develop a new river crossing between Jarrow and East Howdon came to life.

TWITA recognised that the provision of another river crossing would help to free up movement on the region's main road network, would benefit the A19 strategic corridor and could potentially act as a catalyst for the economic regeneration of the north east region. The 1¼ miles (2km) of the original road tunnel was the only section of the 70 mile long A19 route running through North Yorkshire up to Northumberland that was not a dual carriageway.

"The Tyne Tunnel was one of the worst congestion blackspots in the whole of the UK. It was a frustration for drivers and a block on economic development along the strategically important A19 corridor. The need for a second tunnel was obvious" explains Councillor David Wood, the Chairman of TWITA.

TWITA stepped in to take the New Tyne Crossing project over in the mid-1990s, once it had been identified that the preferred option was adjacent to the original Tyne Tunnel. The Tyneside District Councils and TWITA funded a feasibility study that looked at the engineering and funding options for the crossing, which suggested a Private Finance Initiative (PFI) or Public-Private Partnership (PPP) to develop the scheme. TWITA had unsuccessfully sought Government funding to deliver the project. However the Government had indicated that if political will could be demonstrated to back the scheme, a Private Members Bill would be put forward that would enable Tyne Tunnel legislation to be changed so that toll revenues could be used to fund the New Tyne Crossing development costs. This was easily achieved, and the Bill became an Act of Parliament in 1998.

"As the body responsible for the Tyne Tunnel, it was the responsibility of the Tyne & Wear Integrated Transport Authority to plan and deliver a second tunnel, creating new capacity" explains Councillor David Wood, Chairman of TWITA. "The project was a long time in the planning. What the public never see is the work that goes on behind the scenes. We had to secure the necessary legal powers and create the reference design for the scheme, take the project through a public inquiry, a legal challenge, procurement, and monitoring construction to ensure the project met exacting standards.

"At the same time, the Transport Authority team, then later the Concessionaire TT2, had to establish and maintain relationships with hundreds of individuals and organisations, listen to their concerns and ensure the project was managed in such a way as to minimise the impact of construction on lives and business. In this regard I see the New Tyne Crossing as setting new standards in stakeholder engagement."

In addition to the desire to increase capacity at the Tyne Tunnels site, other motivations existed for a second road tunnel. From the late 1980s to the early 2000s the Pedestrian and Cyclist Tunnels and the original vehicular Tyne Tunnel were affected by the introduction of legislation and rule changes arising from tragic situations occurring elsewhere. For the Pedestrian and Cyclist Tunnels the Kings Cross Underground Station fire of 1987 required changes to be implemented, particularly in relation to the use and operation of the wooden escalators. For the vehicular Tyne Tunnel it was the Mont Blanc Tunnel fire in 1999 that provided the impetus for major change. These regulation changes were behind a major safety upgrade of the Pedestrian and Cyclist Tunnels in the mid-1990s and provided an additional significant influence on TWITA in developing the New Tyne Crossing Project.

With the location agreed the next thing to think about was the type of river crossing that should be built. A bridge between Jarrow and East Howdon would need to be very high, to accommodate the large ships entering the Tyne from the North Sea. The span of such a large bridge would be very intrusive and would sever the communities they ran through. This option was therefore soon discounted. With a precedent already set the preferred option was to build another road tunnel.

St. Lawrence, St Anthony's, Walker & St Bede

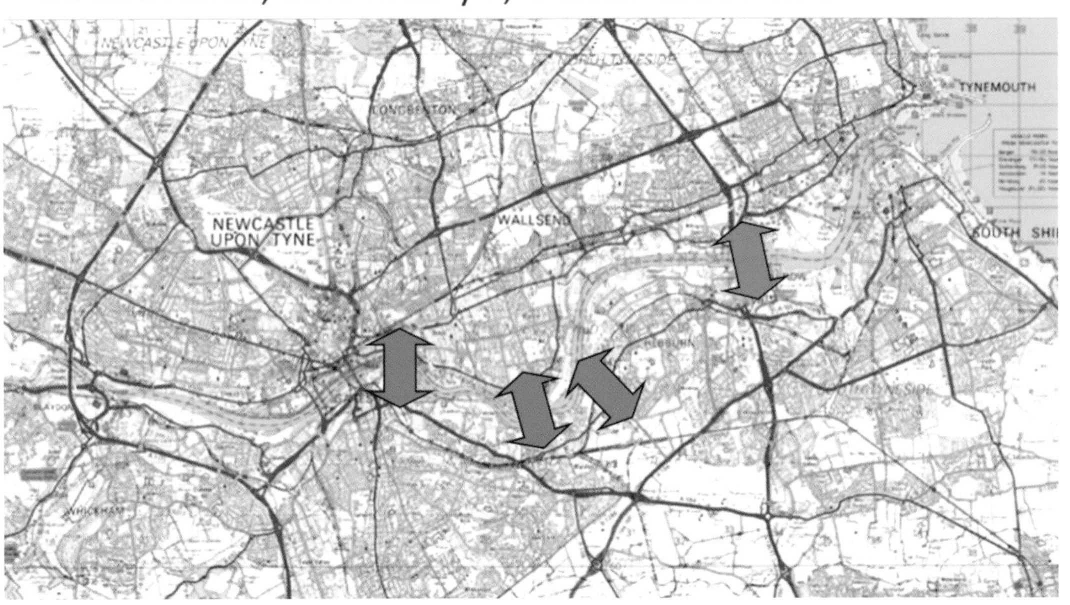

A LONG running and extensive consultation process was undertaken by TWITA to develop the design plans for the new road tunnel.

A feasibility study was carried out in 1996 which demonstrated not only that the New Tyne Crossing project could enable the original road tunnel to be brought up to modern European safety standards, but crucially that the project could be funded solely with private finance. In essence the design and build costs for both the new tunnel and the refurbished older tunnel would be met through toll revenues, under a sophisticated Public Private Partnership agreement.

Amongst the first activities TWITA undertook to progress the project were the setting of development controls for the new scheme, in Autumn 1998. North and South Tyneside Councils made resolutions to protect the land from further developments to save it for the project. TWITA had also set budgets to deal with land issues that might arise, such as matters of blight. An early acquisition was the Gaslight Public House in Jarrow, which TWITA bought as it was situated along the line of the new tunnel, and would face possible demolition.

TWITA also invested a great deal of time procuring a technical advisor, as they didn't have the skills or resources to deliver the scheme in house.

Arup was appointed by the Transport Authority in 1999 to provide assistance in procuring a Public Private Partnership (PPP) type concession to finance and operate the new crossing of the River Tyne without risk to the public sector. The Arup team was pivotal during the evaluation of the private sector bids and the negotiations with bidders leading to the selection of a Preferred Bidder and award of the contract to TT2 Ltd in November 2007.

Malcolm Shaw from Arup was actively involved during delivery of the works. "We were delighted to be a part of a 'local project' which was both of regional and strategic importance to the North East" he explains. " The benefits of the project to the local communities and the region as a whole are self evident and we are proud to have been involved in a project which has already made such a difference to people's lives".

Arup were involved in many aspects of the project including the examination of a number of alternative solutions which eventually led to the selection of the preferred scheme: a second tunnel and the refurbishment of the existing tunnel, to provide a dual carriageway both north and south across the Tyne.

Malcolm recalls "There were many technical challenges, environmental constraints and community issues to be overcome during the development of the Reference Design which was required to demonstrate the feasibility and constructability of the scheme. The chosen design incorporated immersed tube technology to reduce the depth of construction, minimise costs and any effect on the river. We also took into account the proximity of people's homes and businesses and of course the ability to keep the crossing operational throughout the whole of the works. There was no simple solution to this complex problem".

Plans and Preparations

The Transport Authority began consulting with local residents, businesses and the wider community to enable them to understand public views for a new tunnel, and to explain the rationale behind their developing proposal. Paul Fenwick, the Project Director for TWITA, remembers the start of those early consultation sessions. "The first public drop-in events were extremely busy. People were anxious to find out what was being considered and how it would affect them. We answered a lot of questions, but also learned a huge amount about public expectations and concerns. "

At the time of the initial public events no solution had been identified for the south junction of the Tyne Tunnels due to the constraints and technical difficulties at the site. The 1996 feasibility study suggested a particular configuration for the junction, which was very difficult and tortuous, would have required the route to cut through an area of Special Scientific Interest, and would have been expensive to develop. It was also very close to the Lindisfarne Junction, which would have presented operational challenges once built. However there were very few alternatives. TWITA's technical advisor developed two options for the south junction: a refined version of the Lindisfarne route, and a new option, which involved an overbridge very close to the tunnel entrance. The latter option was the better choice in terms of environmental impacts and financial costs. It was also the most efficient choice for accommodating traffic. However this route ran very close to housing in Epinay Walk, and residents there expressed their grave concerns about the proposal. TWITA submitted a report of the options, including impacts and consultation feedback, to South Tyneside Council to reach a final decision on. The Epinay option was selected, and formed part of the final reference design.

THE NEW
TYNE CROSSING
Update
Issue 6 – June 2002

Write time to give your views

Members of the public and organisations have until 19 July to send letters of support or objection about the proposed New Tyne Crossing to the Secretary of State for Transport and the Regions.

Tyne and Wear Passenger Transport Authority (PTA), which is sponsoring the project, supported by North Tyneside and South Tyneside Councils, applied for the necessary powers to build an immersed tube tunnel between Jarrow and Howdon on 31 May.

It is expected that the Secretary of State will call a Public Inquiry for later in the year when all the issues surrounding the construction and future operation of the tunnel will be aired.

Jarrow councillor and PTA deputy vice chair Tom Hanson urged people to write.

"The PTA sees the new tunnel as vital to the whole of Tyne and Wear, but particularly to South Tyneside which has the highest levels of unemployment," he said.

"The vehicular crossings of the Tyne from Blaydon to the existing tunnel are now at capacity most of the day. The New Tyne Crossing will relieve congestion and so eliminate the delays which motorists currently endure at the Tyne Tunnel. It will also, to some extent, ease the situation on other crossings.

PTA vice and deputy vice chairs Muriel Green and Tom Hanson deliver the application to Government Office North East

"The PTA is committed to keeping the public informed about the scheme. We will be holding exhibitions and making the application documents available in several locations.

"I hope people will take the opportunity to find out about the scheme and write to the Secretary of State whether they support it or not."

The address is shown overleaf.

See exhibition venues and times on back page.

While the planning process and consultations were in progress, TWITA began preparing the site for the planned river crossing. In order to clear a path for the new tunnel some properties had to be demolished in central Jarrow, including The Grange nursing home in Staple Road, and St. Peter's Church of England Primary School in Ormonde Street. At a cost of approximately £2 million the school relocated and merged with Ellison Street Church of England Primary School to create the new Jarrow Cross Church of England Primary School. The school's relocation took just over two years to complete, hence it had been important for TWITA to begin the process of relocations and acquisitions even before the planning process had been completed, in order to minimise subsequent delays.

Elsewhere in Jarrow, on High Street, there were demolitions of a number of housing and shop units. TWITA had also developed a discretionary purchase scheme. Property values in Jarrow had started to fall, which some residents felt might be attributable to the New Tyne Crossing project. TWITA did not want local people to be unfairly disadvantaged due to the project and hence developed the discretionary purchase scheme so that those who felt they were experiencing disproportionate hardship could apply for financial relief. Independent house value surveys were also commissioned to ensure that the process was fair and unbiased. Under the discretionary purchase scheme TWITA purchased two properties, which owners were struggling to sell.

Where possible, buildings and structures were protected, including the Grade 2 listed Charles Palmer statue. The statue had been located in

Jarrow's riverside park close to the location of the historic Palmer shipyards. However, due to the secluded and overgrown nature of the park the statue was subject to ongoing vandalism and had become quite damaged. TWITA organised a sensitive renovation of the statue and relocated it to a more prominent position, outside Jarrow Town Hall, where it could be enjoyed by a wider audience and maintained with dignity.

In May 2002 an application was made by the Transport Authority to obtain the necessary powers to enable them to proceed with the New Tyne Crossing project. A Public Inquiry followed, and TWITA suggested that it should be held at the vacant St. Peter's CoE Primary School, which was accessible for the local community and lay on the line of the proposed tunnel route. Plans progressed for the Public Inquiry to take place there, but sadly an arson attack shortly before the Public Inquiry was due to take place made this impossible. The plans were revised, with The Grange nursing home identified as the new venue for the Inquiry. However another arson

Tunnels for everyone

attack, on nearby Dunn Street Primary School, meant that the preference was to offer the nursing home to the school as temporary accommodation while their new facilities were built. Eventually the Public Inquiry was held close to the proposed tunnel site at Jarrow Community Centre between 4 March and 17 April 2003.

While many motorists supported the scheme, their views were not shared by everyone. 608 letters of objection were lodged with the Inquiry, while there were 189 letters of support. At the Inquiry itself, 33 objectors and seven supporters appeared or were represented.

The Public Inquiry addressed the objections to the scheme one by one, many of which were environmentally based. One of the main claims against the new road tunnel was that such an investment would encourage increasing car usage, and hence would be damaging to the environment.

Councillor Muriel Green, who at the time was the Chair of the Transport Authority's Tyne Tunnels Working Group, reported that there was an encouraging level of support for the New Tyne Crossing, which was not only expected to relieve congestion and enhance economic prospects, but which would also allow improvements to be made to public transport connections in the area. It was difficult to maintain a reliable bus service through the Tyne Tunnels due to the peak hour delays. Cllr. Green remarked that "Organisations raising objections at the time of the Public Inquiry were not necessarily opposed to the scheme. Many required clarification on specific issues, or requested that additional work be done to address their concerns."

Having listened to the case for and against the proposal, and examined the raft of accompanying documentation, the Secretary of State for Transport gave the go-ahead for the New Tyne Crossing on 21 July 2005 subject to a few minor modifications to the scheme to take account of issues raised during the Inquiry. Preparations for the project were able to begin in earnest.

Bringing the vision into focus

TENDER documents were issued through the Official Journal of the European Union in 2004. On 1st April 2004 TWITA held an open day for people interested in bidding for the work, and four shortlisted consortia were approved in September 2004. Due to the time it took for the Secretary of State to announce his decision, procurement could not be pursued at that time. It was decided to hold the procurement process while waiting for confirmation of the Order, which was eventually given in July 2005. However, the decision was instantly challenged, and hence procurement was once more delayed.

The Legal Challenge, lodged by a lone protestor against the Secretary of State's decision, related to the disposal of waste arising during the project. The challenger felt that waste routes must be specified in advance. The Secretary of State supported TWITA's view that such details could not be finalised so far in advance, and that in any case the disposal of waste would require licenses to be obtained at the appropriate time, so that controls to protect the environment would not be overlooked. The Legal Challenge was dismissed in May 2006, and procurement could finally be progressed. By this time, two of the consortia had decided to drop out of the bidding process to design and build the New Tyne Crossing.

A group of predominantly North East based firms formed a consortium led by international tunnelling specialist Bouygues TP. It was this consortium that was awarded Preferred Bidder status in April 2007, and in November that year the consortium evolved into the project Concessionaire, TT2 Limited, charged with delivering the scheme over a thirty year period.

The existing Tyne Tunnel staff were transferred over to TT2 employment on 1st February 2008 under a TUPE agreement, moving the operations from local authority control into private sector management. Long discussions involving staff and unions took place in the lead up to transfer to ensure that their views were understood and that a smooth transfer could be agreed. Tyne Tunnel staff were keen to stay in the local government pension scheme and terms and conditions had to be drawn up that could satisfy the various needs. Staff were well informed throughout the process and heavily consulted, so that at the time of transfer it all progressed very smoothly and amicably.

Under the Concession agreement TWITA decides what the toll levels should be, and TT2 collects the tolls on their behalf. A proportion of the toll revenues are paid to TT2, with the remainder staying with TWITA. TWITA is responsible for the major maintenance of the Pedestrian and Cyclist Tunnels, and the toll revenues that TWITA receives from the vehicle tunnels fund these improvement works.

Under the Public-Private Partnership TWITA handed over responsibility to TT2 for:

The design and build of the new Vehicle Tunnel;

The full refurbishment of the original Vehicle Tunnel;

The operation and full maintenance of the Vehicle Tunnels;

The operation and routine maintenance of the Pedestrian and Cyclist tunnels.

New Tyne Crossing Ambitions

DURING the tender process TWITA specified a set of objectives that they wanted the successful consortium to try to achieve whilst delivering t he New Tyne Crossing project.

These were as follows, and TT2 committed to meeting these objectives from the outset:

TWITA objectives - list

(A) Build and operate a new tunnel to conform to safety requirements and refurbish and operate the existing tunnels to best practice consistent with their construction and listed status.

(B) Facilitate the amicable transfer of Tyne Tunnel Employees to the concessionaire

(C) Minimise the actual toll level charged to users – including maintaining the current zero VAT rating

(D) Promote public transport, cycle and pedestrian use of the Tunnels

(E) Procure the New Tyne Crossing in the most cost effective manner

(F) Minimise the environmental and social impact of the tunnel on local residents and businesses, both during construction and operation

(G) Protect and promote the ecology of the Tyne and its tributaries as an important element of the region's environment

(H) Minimise disruption to the operation of the existing tunnels during construction

(I) Support local communities during construction by regular involvement and intervention to minimise disruption

(J) Incentivise the Concessionaire to complete the construction processes as soon as practicable

(K) Allow flexibility in Term of the Concession i.e. between 30 years and 40 years to facilitate the above objectives

(L) Support the Port of Tyne as the Road, Rail and Marine Freight Hub for the North East Region

(M) Pro-actively communicate and liaise with all affected authorities, agencies, land owners and communities to foster good relations and understanding of the project and the TWPTA's objectives

Tunnel facts:

Total project length (including approach roads): 2.65 km

Length of new road tunnel: 1.5 km

Length of river section: 360m

Width of tunnel carriageway: 7.3m

How the new tunnel was built

THE second Tyne vehicle tunnel was the third in the UK to be built using the immersed tube technique, the others being the Conwy and Medway tunnels.

This was an entirely different technique to that used in building the first road tunnel and the Pedestrian and Cyclist Tunnels, which had been created using traditional tunnelling techniques and excavation under compressed air.

The river section of the tunnel is made up of the immersed tube tunnel elements. The land tunnels north and south of the Tyne were predominantly built using a cut-and-cover technique, with other methods used where conditions dictated a different approach. The scale of the scheme meant that the construction site was subdivided into four manageable areas: the North Approach, the River Section, the South Tunnel, and the South Junction.

Building the new tunnel - Cut and cover

The majority of the land tunnels were built using a technique known as cut-and-cover. In simple terms this involves building the tunnel at the bottom of a trench. Once the tunnel is built the trench is refilled with soil.

The first stage of the cut and cover technique involved building reinforced concrete walls underground, along the length of the future road tunnel. These underground, or "diaphragm", walls were created by excavating two parallel trenches approximately one metre wide and up to 33 metres deep. As they were being dug out a liquid clay called bentonite was pumped into the narrow trench to prevent it from re-filling with soil. Bentonite tanks were installed either side of the river to supply the diaphragm wall excavations.

As the excavation of the trenches continued betonite was continually pumped into the space being created, helping the trench to keep its shape.

Geotechnical specialist Bachy Soletanche was responsible for building the underground 'cut & cover' walls for the new tunnel, to a depth of 33m in places

Geotechnical specialist Bachy Soletanche was responsible for carrying out the diaphragm wall works for the new vehicle tunnel on both sides of the river. This involved 700 metres of cut and cover tunnel on the south side of the river and 400 metres to the north.

Once the excavations had reached the desired depth and length Bachy Soletanche constructed reinforcement cages, which were lowered into the trenches. The cages were essentially made of sheets of metal mesh that provided the mould for the concrete walls. Once the reinforcement cages were installed concrete could be pumped into the excavated space. Concrete is heavier than bentonite, so that as it was poured into the trench it sank to the bottom, pushing the bentonite out at the top. The displaced bentonite was pumped back into the tanks, having served its temporary purpose. In this way the reinforced underground walls were built. Once the concrete had hardened, the diaphragm walls provided a dual role: as well as assisting the construction process, by helping to prevent the excavated space from moving, they also formed the final tunnel walls. The rough surface of the diaphragm walls can be seen by motorists using the tunnel today.

The walls varied in depth from 17 metres to 33 metres along the length of the tunnel. This difference in depths is partly because the tunnel must travel deeper underground towards the river, in order to enable motorists to travel from the ground surface to a route beneath the Tyne. However, the wall depth was also affected by the ground conditions, or geology. In some places the wall extends further beneath the tunnel base in order to provide greater stability.

During construction of the diaphragm walls Bachy Soletanche obtained additional rigs to the New Tyne Crossing site, from other group companies in France and Spain, in order to meet the tight project programme. Whilst the amount of equipment on site enabled work to progress quickly, it did present some challenges due to the limited space available. Bachy Soletanche's Project Manager, Clare Doby, explained that "The site was logistically challenging. It was long and narrow and could become very crowded. We had to build our reinforcement cages off site because there simply wasn't room to do it close to the excavations. This meant it was vital to forward plan carefully and follow a very strict programme so that everything was well coordinated. That said, the complexities made it a very exciting and fascinating scheme to work on."

Once the concrete diaphragm walls had set the main tunnel excavations could begin.

With the diaphragm walls creating the boundaries of a reinforced underground space the area between the walls was excavated, to a width of approximately fifteen metres, and down to a depth of up to 33 metres near the river's edge. Hydraulic struts (props) were used to temporarily support the excavation. The struts prevented the walls from moving as a result of the immense ground pressure created by an excavation of such depth. Due to the challenging circumstances at the site, partly caused by the depth of the excavation and also the poor ground conditions, a bespoke strut was especially designed for the job, with a 500 tonne capacity. Layers of struts were installed as the excavation went deeper underground.

With the struts in place, and tunnel excavations complete, construction of the tunnel itself could begin. The floor slab was laid at the base of the trench and formwork was installed in the shape of the internal tunnel corridors and roof panels. Concrete was poured into moulds around the formwork to create the reinforced tunnel structure.

The diaphragm walls extend deeper into the ground beyond the tunnel floor slabs, creating additional support for the tunnel structure by acting as foundations into the ground below.

The height of the tunnel varies along its length, as does the gradient (or slope) of the tunnel. To help pour the concrete roof panels, a specially made mobile formwork was used. This was effectively a mould on wheels that could be moved along the length of the tunnel to adapt to the height and slope of the tunnel at any location. Once in place it would provide the vessel for concreting the walls of the escape passage.

Once the tunnel had been built at the bottom of the cut-and-cover trench the props above the tunnel were removed and the trench re-filled with soil. The soil above the tunnel is compacted to provide permanent support above the tunnel.

At the deepest part of the cut-and-cover tunnel, near Jarrow's riverside, a second roof panel was installed mid-way between the tunnel structure and the ground surface, in order to relieve ground pressure upon the tunnel.

HUNTLEY
MANITOU
MANITOU

Sprayed Concrete Lining Tunnels

Two sections of the land tunnel through Jarrow were built using a technique called Sprayed Concrete Lining (SCL). These sections were introduced to avoid major utility disruptions. Beneath Jarrow's riverside park a gas main crosses the route of the new road tunnel. Further south, just beyond the ventilation shaft serving the original vehicle tunnel, a major combined sewer runs across the site. The diversions required to relocate these vital services would have been substantial, time consuming, and costly. The obvious choice was to tunnel beneath these services. Nonetheless, despite their relatively short length (37 metres and 46 metres each) the SCL technique brought its own challenges, particularly as a result of the ground conditions beneath Jarrow.

SCL is a tunnelling technique that involves excavating the tunnel and spraying the excavation with concrete as work proceeds, to create an instant outer (or primary) tunnel lining. This maintains the shape of the excavation and minimises ground movement. Once the primary tunnel lining was in place it was supplemented with a secondary, strengthening lining and a waterproofing layer. The SCL sections also required additional fire protection measures, applied with fire boards. The metre thick diaphragm walls in the cut and cover tunnels provided an in-built level of fire protection because of the thickness of the concrete. However the SCL tunnels feature a much thinner layer of concrete (approximately 750mm thick), so that extra fire protection was needed.

A complication encountered with the SCLs for the new Tyne Tunnel arose as a result of the geological conditions. The ground through Jarrow features laminated clays, which are thin layers of clay that were inclined to slide and move as the ground was excavated for the SCL tunnels. This movement created difficulties in attempting to set the sprayed concrete lining. The decision was taken to inject the ground with grout prior to excavation in order to solidify and stabilise it, and this enabled the work to take place more easily.

As the SCL tunnels were built separately from the surrounding cut and cover sections of tunnel, dividing walls were in place between them. It was seen as a milestone achievement when the dividing walls between the SCLs and the adjoining tunnel were broken through, to create a unified link.

Building above the first road tunnel

There is one section of the new tunnel that lies only a few metres above the original road tunnel. North of river the 1967-built tunnel follows a 360 degree turn as it makes the steep ascent up to ground level. The new road tunnel is a straighter, shallower river crossing and it passes above the original tunnel at that point. There is a vertical distance of approximately 2.5 metres between the roof of the old tunnel and the base of the foundations for the new tunnel.

With such a small vertical distance between the two tunnels it was not possible to use exactly the same technique for the cut and cover tunnel as in other places. The original tunnel has been in situ since 1967, designed to withstand the weight of the ground lying above it. Removing the soil above the original tunnel would have relieved the substantial ground pressure that had existed upon the structure for more than forty years, which would have resulted in movement of the old tunnel structure. It was therefore absolutely vital that the pressure upon the existing tunnel structure was maintained, whilst constructing the new tunnel above it.

The approach used to overcome this challenge was a "top down" technique, whereby the roof of the tunnel was built before the area beneath was excavated.

The roof structure at this cross-over point was built first,

The original road tunnel was monitored for structural movement throughout the construction works. The monitoring equipment showed that the tunnel barely moved during the works, proving that the technique had been successful.

Gulls halt progress

The Gas Light public house stood close to the line of the cut and cover tunnel in Jarrow's riverside park. It was a Grade 2 listed building because it had some local historic interest, having served the shipbuilding community for decades. Most notably local legend suggests that the building was used to hide the body of William Jobling after it was removed from a gibbet at Jarrow Slake in 1832.

Due to the proximity of the public house to the tunnel works it was decided to demolish the building, as the building was not considered likely to be able to withstand the construction\ works and excavations so close by. The building had been vacant for quite some time, and archaeologists had not identified anything of significant interest in or around the site.

Plans to demolish the building were put on hold, however, when Herring Gulls took roost in the building's chimney pot. Work around the Gas Light pub was postponed for several weeks until the chicks had flown the nest.

A new tunnel for a modern era

Dredging a route under the Tyne

THE original road tunnel was built by cutting into the bedrock more than 15 metres below the riverbed. The new tunnel, however, is far shallower. It is worth noting however that the tunnel does lie beneath the river bed, and is not lying on top of it, which was a popular myth during construction.

The original proposal for dredging the river bed was to use a bucket dredger. Large enough to hold two Mini Cooper cars, the bucket scoop attached to the dredger would have cut into the river bed and pulled the waste material up through the water to the surface, to be dumped upon a barge and disposed of at sea. This approach had been approved through Public Inquiry.

Just before dredging was due to start Bouygues TP identified a better way of dredging the river bed and disposing of the waste. Port of Tyne had indicated that they were looking to redevelop their Victorian Tyne Dock. No longer large enough to accommodate modern sea vessels, the Port had decided to infill the dock so that the area could be reused for other purposes. Port of Tyne were looking for 500,000 cubic metres of material to infill the dock. Dredging of the river bed would generate an estimated 400,000 cubic metres. It was therefore decided to look into an entirely different technique for carving the tunnel route into the river bed, using a cutter suction dredger.

Cutter suction dredging involves excavating a trench into the river bed and simultaneously sucking the debris into a floating pipeline, to avoid any material being dragged through the water column. In some ways the technique can be compared to a domestic household vacuum cleaner.

The cutter suction dredger is a specialised type of ship, fitted with a cutting head approximately 1 metre wide, which rotates and cuts a trench into the riverbed. The dredger is also fitted with powerful suction equipment, connected to the cutting head via pipeline. As the cutting head rotates and creates its excavation in the riverbed, the debris is instantly sucked away via pipeline, so that almost no waste material is released into the water. The pipeline

connected the tunnel site to Tyne Dock, so that waste removed from the dredged river bed was transported direct to the dock, where it was used to fill in the empty dock space.

Benefits of cutter suction dredging

A smaller footprint: Using this technique it was not necessary to close the shipping route along the River Tyne while dredging works took place. This meant that river users were able to go about their business with minimal impact, which was good for the local and regional economy.

Quicker: Furthermore the technique was far quicker than the originally proposed bucket dredger approach, reducing the timescale from an estimated six months to just five weeks. This further limited the potential impact of the dredging activities on other river users.

Cleaner: Just as importantly the River Tyne, at the time of dredging, was considered the best salmon fishing river in England and Wales. It was therefore vital that every effort was taken to protect the water quality and environment for migratory fish. It was also important that fish migration routes were not impeded, and that the dredging technique itself would not directly harm the fish.

Salmon-friendly: The cutter suction technique was far cleaner than the industry standard bucket dredger, with almost all waste passing directly into the dredger's pipeline rather than into the river's water column. This helped to maintain pre-dredging water quality standards. Furthermore, as dredging activity was limited to the river bed migratory fish were able to continue their journeys along the Tyne in the upper parts of the river without interruption. Salmon migration tends to occur in the upper parts of the water rather than near the riverbed, hence this technique was ideally suited to fish migration routes.

Strict controls had been in place to allow the impacts of dredging to be monitored. Water quality levels were recorded upstream and downstream of the dredging site, as well as close to the area of dredging, before, during and after the works. Fish counters were also installed to monitor impacts on fish numbers. This data was made publicly available through a dedicated website so that any pollution incidents could be identified immediately, and so that all activities were open to scrutiny.

The dredging works were very successful. The Environment Agency released post-dredging salmon figures which revealed that during the year following dredging the best ever counts of salmon had been recorded in the Tyne.

Re-use of waste: By using the cutter suction approach the project was able to avoid disposing of any waste at licensed sites out at sea. It had only proved possible to use this technique because of the availability of a nearby site within which to dispose of the dredged materials. Port of Tyne had expressed the need to source material to fill their Victorian Tyne Dock, located 2.5 kms downstream from the New Tyne Crossing site. The dock was too small to accommodate most modern freight vessels and hence was to be redeveloped. This was an ideal opportunity to reuse the 400,000 cubic metres of river dredged waste. A floating pipeline was attached to the cutter suction dredger to directly transport all dredged materials direct into Tyne Dock, thereby not only avoiding the disposal of waste but also supporting local regeneration.

Community benefits:

Environmental surveys carried out before works began revealed that around 10% of the material to be dredged from the river bed was contaminated as a result of previous heavy industry on the Tyne. The contaminated matter was concentrated on the southern side of the river, and under original proposals this material was to be removed and treated on site, before being transported by road for disposal at a landfill site. This would have required an estimated 4500 lorry loads of material to be driven through Jarrow for disposal elsewhere. Instead, this waste was the first to be dredged and carefully contained within the dock. Environmental controls were put in place and monitoring undertaken to ensure that none of the contaminants could be released into the water.

Use of cutter suction dredging prevented the transportation and disposal of around 40,000 cubic metres of material. This was positive for the people living and working in Jarrow, and beneficial for the environment.

DID YOU KNOW?.... that the most difficult material for the cutter head to remove wasn't the bedrock beneath the Tyne but supermarket shopping trolleys!

P43.

Building the caissons

THE river section of the new road tunnel was made up of four concrete tunnel tubes, which were lowered into the trench that had been dredged into the bed of the Tyne.

The tunnel tubes, or caissons, were built in a dry dock by VolkerStevin Marine, the lead contractor for the construction, and subsequent immersion, of the caissons. Early investigations into a suitable dock found no potential locations near the tunnel site. The closest possible dock, large enough to accommodate construction of the four caissons, was thirty miles away. However, a disused dry dock was identified on the Tyne. The Walker dry dock was slightly too small to suit the construction works, yet it was located only 4 km upstream from the tunnel site. Building the caissons there would have brought great advantages in terms of liaising with the different project teams and for transportation of the river tunnel units to their final destination. There was also the opportunity to bring investment to Tyneside, in line with project commitments to maximise local involvement in the scheme.

Due to the advantages associated with the Tyneside dock it was eventually decided to slightly amend the tunnel's reference design to enable use of the dry dock at Walker. By building up the river banks at Jarrow and East Howdon the caissons could be slightly shorter than originally planned, enabling construction to fit within the Walker dry dock. However, the space constraints at the site presented challenges of their own. Gerrit Smit, Project Manager for VolkerStevin Marine, explained "The new Tyne Tunnel is by no means the largest immersed tube tunnel we have built, yet it was a very challenging one. The units were fairly small, and had to be built in a very restricted dock, which forced us to operate in a strictly controlled and carefully coordinated manner. It is similar to the difference between building dolls house furniture and adult furniture. It is far more intricate and fiddly!"

In addition the smaller units were heavier than larger tubes would have been, with smaller air-filled spaces inside.

Before the tunnel units could be built the dry dock had to be prepared. Having lain unused for many years, it was first necessary to reinstall the dock gate, and then to empty the dock. Water and debris from the dock were pumped directly into an adjacent, closed dock until dock number 4 was clean and ready for use.

The dock was first filled with a gravel bed. Eight tonnes of gravel were poured in to the dock to create a base that could be curved to match the profile of the river bed. Hard flooring was subsequently placed on the gravel bed, and the formwork for the four caissons was quickly erected above this.

The caissons are built of reinforced concrete. Each 90m long caisson was made up of four sections, and each of these sections required two concrete pours: one pour for the base of the section, and one continuous pour for the walls and roof. In total the four caissons required 32 concrete pours and 14,400 cubic metres of concrete. A series of pipes was built into the caisson formwork to allow cooling water to be circulated while the concrete was poured. This kept the concrete at the correct temperature, enabling it to set properly.

DID YOU KNOW?....
it took 16 hours to pour the walls and roof for each of the four sections making up a caisson.

Tunnel facts:
Length of each caisson: 90m
Width of each caisson: 15m
Height of each caisson: 8m
Weight of each caisson: 10,000 tonnes
Length of Walker Dry Dock: 210 m

TY
NE

VolkerStevin Marine used immersed tube technology to place the tunnel sections in the river bed. The contract involved the manufacture, transportation and immersion of the four tunnel caissons

Internally the caissons were built to include separate sections for the pedestrian escape passage and, above it, the service corridor to house the tunnel's utilities. Temporary "bulk head" walls were built at either end of each caisson to close them and help them float during transportation. These temporary walls were removed once the caissons were fully installed in the pre-dredged trench.

Flotation

Once the caissons were built, and the trench in the riverbed dredged, the individual tunnel elements could be floated along the River Tyne and lowered into place.

Flotation from the dry dock occurred during January and February 2010, during one of the most severe winters on record. Before the caissons could be towed out of the dock, it was necessary to flood the dock. The sluice gates were opened on 12 December 2009 by Chairman of TWITA, Councillor David Wood, and Project Director for Bouygues TP, Nicolas Caille. It took around four hours for the dock to fill with water.

The first tunnel unit was floated from the dry dock in January 2010. Due to the dimensions of the dock, and the close

proximity of the caissons to one another, and to the dock walls, removing the first caisson was a complex and challenging procedure. The process was complicated by the fact that the entrance to the dock included a lip, which protruded from the floor of the dock. This meant the caissons had to be lifted above the lip to avoid damaging the base of the unit, as well as avoiding impacts to any of the walls.

The timing of each flotation was therefore carefully calculated to work with the tidal movements in the river, using high water levels to help with the movement of the caisson over the dock lip. There was a window of only a few hours within which to remove the first caisson. During one very cold

January afternoon the first caisson was slowly and very carefully pulled from the dock by tug boat. Once free from the dock the caisson was attached to two further tug boats, and the three vessels manoeuvred the caisson downstream to the Tyne Tunnels site, where it was moored until ready to be lowered beneath the water.

There was a period of two weeks between the flotation of each caisson. With the first caisson removed, subsequent flotations were much easier to facilitate, due to the extra space available within the dry dock.

Immersion

Despite weighing in at 10,000 tonnes each, the caissons were naturally inclined to float rather than sink in the water. Filled with air, this was not altogether surprising. Therefore, in order to lower the caissons to their riverbed destinations it was necessary to fit each unit with ballast tanks so that water could be temporarily added to the tanks to add sufficient weight to the caissons to enable them to be sunk.

Five ballast tanks were placed in each caisson and approximately 2,850 m3 water, with 30 m3 of trim concrete, was placed into the tanks to ballast, or

weigh down, each caisson.

As with the flotation sequence, which took place at spring tide, there was a period of two weeks between the immersion of each caisson, which coincided with neap tide. Above the water there was little to see during the immersion process, with all attention focused on underwater activities. The first caisson was positioned adjacent to the Jarrow riverbank. It was lowered into position using anchoring equipment and GPS (Global Positioning System) satellite based technology, as well as specialised divers to ensure the precise positioning of the caisson against the land tunnel.

Lowering into place

One of the complexities associated with lowering the caissons at this point in the River Tyne was the mixture of the river's freshwater and the North Sea's more buoyant saltwater. This could create uneven buoyancy which further complicated the delicate process of lowering the unit perfectly into place.

The final caisson was lowered into place on 23rd February 2010, one year before the new Vehicle Tunnel would come into operation.

Despite all caissons being in place, the river section was not quite complete however. In order to provide room to manoeuvre each caisson into position in the river bed trench, a short section of the river tunnel had been left unconstructed. This section was built in situ, underwater, once all the caissons had been installed. Specialised divers were needed to help with this task.

Before placing the last two caissons, steel formwork was placed on the river bed. Both caissons were positioned on top of this formwork when they were lowered into place. Once all caissons were located beneath the river the gap of approximately 2.5 metres between the last two caissons was closed by placing steel formwork to the sides and on top of the structure. Inside the caissons provisions were made to ensure a tight fit between the caisson and the formwork. Once the formwork had been checked by divers, the gap between the caissons was pumped dry, helping to strengthen the watertight seal. Concrete was poured to close the gap, from inside the caissons.

How the river caissons connect together

Each caisson was fitted, prior to flotation, with a 'Gina' seal at each end. Two layers of seals were used, an outer and inner seal, the Omega seal being added as the secondary seal. The fitting overall was designed, like a jigsaw, to connect to the seal of the adjacent caisson or land tunnel. The seals were joined together on the riverbed during immersion of the caissons. Once connected, the water trapped between the seals was pumped out, causing hydrostatic pressure to hold the caissons together.

Reshaping the complex south junction

THE south junction was originally known within the project as the complex junction. From the tunnel portal in Jarrow there were 400 metres of planned road works at the south junction, designed to improve traffic flow through the restricted site.

One of the factors impeding traffic flow at the south junction had been the "hamburger" roundabout. In addition to accommodating traffic around the roundabout from standard approaches, there was an extra feature complicating traffic movements. An additional lane for local traffic created a roundabout shortcut, enabling vehicles approaching the junction from Jarrow to cut across the roundabout and go to the front of the Tyne Tunnel queue. This disrupted flow, created traffic tensions, and arguably encouraged rat running through local streets. The plans for the second road tunnel included removal of this notorious roundabout.

With motorists continuing to use the south junction throughout delivery of the scheme, the project engineers worked in close partnership with the Tyne Tunnel operations staff and the project's communications team to carefully coordinate activities so that traffic flow would not be impeded by building works. Colas was appointed to coordinate and implement the traffic management plans during the project, and close liaison with the Colas teams on site ensured that impacts on motorists were minimised, despite the complexity and scale of works required.

The fundamental aim of improvements to the junction was to distinguish local traffic from through traffic, so that neither impeded the other's flow. Ultimately A19 Tyne Tunnel traffic would flow directly into and out of the tunnel, without stopping at the junction, and local traffic would join and leave the A19 via dedicated slip roads. This required the A19 route to be straightened, once the hamburger roundabout had been removed.

The once dominant central 'hamburger' roundabout was removed during construction, and traffic moved through a sequence of road alignments to accommodate the construction works. A smaller roundabout was built to the east of the original roundabout, to facilitate traffic transfer between the A19 and South Tyneside's local roads.

A tunnel with bridges!

The redevelopment of the south junction required new road bridges to be built, so that local road users and A19 through traffic could be kept apart. One of the biggest challenges faced in restructuring the south junction was that of maintaining traffic flow at

an already heavily congested site. It is considered a significant feat that as a result of careful coordination of works between the TT2 traffic staff, the Bouygues TP construction teams, and Colas, journey times through the junction were actually improved upon during the period of building works. Dennis Gregg, Colas North Business Manager, reflected that "At the peak of works, motorists were confronted with hundreds of traffic cones directing them along redefined routes in order to reach their destination. We installed around twice as much signage than we needed to, to make sure that the regular travellers, those who were almost on auto pilot, were clearly directed onto the new temporary route. It was certainly challenging to keep traffic moving through such a busy site while at the same time switching traffic around so frequently to allow building works to take place. Fortunately a great team ethic helped us to achieve this with great success."

During the construction phase only two full tunnel closures were required. The first, during July 2009, was a weekend closure to enable the central bridge beams of the two new bridges to be laid above the A19. Thirteen 28m long concrete beams, each weighing up to 39 tonnes, were placed across the central section of the Epinay Loop Road by a 350 tonne crane positioned on the A19 carriageway. At the same time two lots of seventeen concrete beams, each approximately 25 metres in length and weighing up to 30 tonnes, were placed across the east and west sections of the replacement Howard Street Bridge.

The second weekend tunnel closure, a year later, was necessary to allow the original Howard Street Bridge to be demolished. The new Howard Street Bridge was required as part of the project to create sufficient turning space for vehicles using the roundabout at the top of the Epinay Loop Road. The new Howard Street Bridge is also higher than its predecessor, providing more headroom for tunnel vehicles below. Once the replacement bridge was complete and open to traffic, the original could be removed.

Approving the Works

Despite overall planning permission for the scheme having been provided in 2005, there was nonetheless a requirement for approximately 250 different consents and approvals during the design and build phase.

PS2.

Colas designed and managed a complex range of traffic plans to enable construction progress with minimal disruption.

Parsons Brinckerhoff was appointed by Bouygues TP to manage the approvals and consents process. Project Director, Paul Littlefair spearheaded an innovative, integrated approach for the New Tyne Crossing project: "The challenge was huge. We had to both build and climb the mountain that represented all of the approvals and consents for the project, at the same time. The solution was to integrate the approvals through a collaborative network.

"Approval for the scheme through Public Inquiry bound the build process to a great many approvals, which were intended to protect both the community and the environment. These approvals were effectively a control measure, but achieving them was not straight forward – it was a complex puzzle that required so many different aspects to line up before we could proceed. To manage this challenge, the project was broken down into 4 sections; each section was built over a number of phases, and the phases all added towards the final 'solution' over a 5 year period. It was a huge achievement to complete a challenge of this scale and complexity without delays."

The process involved bringing together the most relevant people from local authorities to clarify their controls and expectations, and to highlight any particular local sensitivities that should be considered in implementing the proposals. Regular approvals workshops were held with the local authorities and project teams to ensure that each party had a clear understanding of each others' perspectives. This led to a smooth consents process and helped to keep the project on track.

Building on polystyrene

Ground conditions at the south junction of the tunnel site, in Jarrow, are weak with marshy areas. The junction had previously been built on engineered piles to provide sufficient strength and stability to withstand the weight created by the large number of vehicles moving through the junction. The weight of the highway structures themselves also required support.

In redesigning the junction the decision was taken to replace the numerous piles with a lightweight fill material, capable of withstanding the weight placed upon the junction yet light enough to avoid sinking into the soft ground below. An encapsulated polystyrene material was used to create the foundation for the south junction, providing strength without weight, and spreading the load evenly across the material.

The same type of material was used above the northbound tunnel's entrance portal, to create a light yet tough cover, enabling the land above the portal to be reclaimed.

The safest tunnel in the UK

Once the tunnel was built it was ready to be kitted out with a range operating and safety systems designed to manage three distinct aspects: the road space (both within the tunnel and all approach roads and plazas within the site); the infrastructure (all structures, plant, equipment and systems); and the people (customers, staff and all contractors - in fact everyone who comes onto the Tyne Tunnels site).

One of the most exciting pieces of technology to be introduced to the new tunnel was the Fixed Fire Suppression System, an intense mist system designed to control a fire in the tunnel and to stop temperatures from rising, rather than to extinguish the flames. The mist system was the first of its kind to be installed in a British tunnel, and was a strong desire by Tyne and Wear Fire and Rescue Service.

Hence the new Vehicle Tunnel became known as the safest tunnel in the country when it opened, thanks to the state-of-the-art fire safety system it features. Both vehicle tunnels have been fitted with the mist system, creating a safer environment for North East motorists.

As well as the mist system the new Vehicle Tunnel was treated to a whole host of leading edge technology. An Incident Detection system linked to a comprehensive and overlapping network of Closed Circuit cameras provides automatic alerts for any unexpected occurrences in the tunnel. This might include a change in visibility levels, suggesting the presence of smoke in the tunnel, or the presence of pedestrians. The Incident Detection system is also linked to the mist system, so that the presence of smoke within the tunnel will automatically induce the mist system to activate, unless the Duty Controller overrides the command.

Additional safety features include the separate and dedicated escape corridor, built into the new tunnel, to protect people needing to leave their cars in emergency situations, and exit the tunnel on foot. The escape passage provides a clean air space with air pressure levels slightly higher than in the road tunnel. The difference in air pressure stops smoke from entering the escape passage, and feels like a brisk breeze to those entering the escape passage.

A breath of fresh air

When there was only one vehicle tunnel, operating bi-directionally (one lane of traffic in each direction), two ventilation buildings were required. The original ventilation chimney in Jarrow served the main length of the first road tunnel, while the chimney in East Howdon served the circular northern end of the tunnel.

Once two tunnels became available, each offering two lanes of one-way traffic, the tunnel ventilation system could operate more efficiently. With all traffic moving in the same direction, the ventilation system could work in harmony with the direction of air flow arising from the vehicles travelling through the tunnel. As a result only one ventilation building is required for each tunnel. The new tunnel is served by a specialised ventilation building built at the south junction, whereas the original tunnel uses the existing ventilation chimney located north of the Tyne.

Air quality monitors are fitted throughout the new

and the refurbished vehicle tunnels with detection sensors so that the ventilation fans will automatically come into use if air quality levels drop.

Tunnel Control

Since the opening of the first road tunnel in 1967 the Tyne Tunnels have benefited from an on-site control room staffed around the clock by highly trained Duty Traffic Controllers.

Over the years there have been several refurbishments of the control room, but the most impressive to date came as part of the New Tyne Crossing project. A state-of-the-art control room was installed, boasting a wide range of leading edge technologies.

Vital Technology was tasked with designing and building the full computer control system (known as SCADA) and data communications at the Tyne Tunnels. The fully integrated system enables TT2 to control the CCTV cameras, telecoms, radio rebroadcasting, traffic management, and safety control systems. With Vital Technology's equipment in place, the Tyne Tunnel controllers are able to safely and effectively manage the entire site from the new control room.

Ematics, a Vital Technology company, was tasked with the design and build of a new Supervisory Control And Data Acquisition (SCADA) computer system and the data communications for the twin tunnel New Tyne Crossing project.

When in operation, the fully-integrated system enables traffic controllers to monitor and operate CCTV cameras, telecoms, radio rebroadcasting, traffic management, and safety control systems for the whole site, safely and effectively from within the new control room.

Paul Ward, director of Vital Technology and Ematics commented: "Designing a system which integrated all of TT2's management tools into one required a great deal of planning and co-ordination.

"It was a complex and unique challenge, given the sensitivity required to implement a brand new system into the tunnel, which couldn't be tested until vehicles started using the new route. This meant we were challenged with motorists in a new environment and controllers using brand new technology under extremely high demand.

"Excessive testing of the system in virtual environments prior to installation made the transition during site installation much smoother and the system worked exactly as we anticipated during the final 'go live' days."

The technology introduced to the new control room has vastly enhanced the speed at which the Duty Controllers can make informed decisions, and enables them to manage all manner of incidents occurring in or around the Tyne Tunnels.

In June 2012 floods hit the North East of England causing widespread road closures across the region. Thanks to the equipment installed at the Tyne Tunnels the Duty Controllers were able to swiftly and effectively respond to the increasingly alarming situation. Ron Henderson, the Tyne Tunnel Manager, explains "Neither of the vehicle tunnels has ever been forced to close because of rising water levels. In fact, during severe winter weather the tunnels are often one of the few passable roads when ice and snow cause problems elsewhere. On this particular occasion, our Duty Controllers were aware of severe problems on the wider highways network and were monitoring the situation across our site, from the control room. They noticed flood water beginning to enter the northbound tunnel. The rate at which water was flowing into the tunnels, from both ends, increased very rapidly. Within a matter of minutes the Controllers took the decision to close the tunnel entirely. The technology they had at their fingertips enabled them to make an informed decision very quickly and to implement a closure of the tunnel as soon as they needed to. This situation might have been very different without such a high tech system in place, and the response would certainly have been slower.

"The greater level of surveillance enabled the controllers to see the bigger picture, as well as gaining detailed insight of what was occurring on our site. With this enhanced knowledge the Duty Controllers were able to manage access and egress to prevent customers from being stranded. It meant that none of our customers were stranded in the rising flood waters."

Vital Technology & Ematics designed, built and integrated the SCADA and Data Communications, enabling complete control and monitoring of interfacing systems from the Tyne Tunnel control room.

Greening the site: landscaping

Before construction of the new road tunnel began preparatory work got underway along the length of the site. By March 2008 all vegetation lying within the construction corridor had been removed to make way for the building works. It was important that this work was carried out during winter months, before the nesting season had started, so as to minimise wildlife impacts.

Part of the commitment within the project was to replace every tree that had been removed with an equivalent of indigenous (native) origin. Many of the species that had been removed prior to construction had been of low ecological value. The plan was to improve the landscape along the entire length of the corridor with plant species that would support wildlife biodiversity and enhance the landscape for local people. A major public consultation exercise was undertaken by the project partners during 2009 to find out how the public would like to see the area re-landscaped once work on the new road tunnel had finished. Hundreds of suggestions were submitted through public drop-in events, written feedback, and dedicated forums with special interest groups including the local Youth Parliament and cycling groups.

In addition to replanting the space accommodated by construction works the project also aimed to open extra land up for public use. The entrance portal of the original road tunnel had featured a honeycomb roof, designed to allow filtered light to enter the tunnel. This had the effect of creating a transition zone for motorists, making it easier for eyes to adjust to the different lighting levels within the tunnel and outside. The refurbishment of the original tunnel saw the honeycomb sun visor replaced with a solid roof, and the transitional lighting zone provided by artificial lighting. Above the tunnel lightweight polystyrene fill was used to build up the land so that, with a deep covering of top soil, it could be opened up for public enjoyment as part of the landscape masterplan.

Did you know the Tyne Tunnels site has a dedicated wildlife area, with bird, bat and squirrel boxes as well as a viewing hide. Look out for Tyne Tunnel beehives, which are part of future plans for the site.

Earthworks

One million cubic metres of earth were moved during the project, to make way for the new tunnel.

The project team worked closely with the Environment Agency to agree where the waste material could be disposed of, and how much of it could be returned to the land.

From the outset there was a determination to make use of the material in a positive way rather than disposing of it as waste. Opportunities to reuse the excavated soil were actively sought, and reworking of the landscape both north and south of the river enabled the vast majority of material to be reused. All of the material dredged from the river was reused to infill Tyne Dock. By the end of the project it was hard to imagine that a complex, major construction site had once stood in place of the landscape that has been left behind.

The role of the toll

The New Tyne Crossing project required no finance from Central Government. The £260 Million scheme was entirely self-funded, and is ultimately paid for by the people who use it, through toll revenues. As a private road it is vital that tolls continue to be collected, to cover the costs associated with the New Tyne Crossing project, as well as providing the funds to pay for the operation and maintenance of all four Tyne Tunnels, and also a major refurbishment of the Pedestrian and Cyclist Tunnels in 2013.

As part of the project two new toll plazas were built, both on the north bank of the Tyne. The eight lane northbound toll plaza lies close to the exit of the older vehicle tunnel, collecting tolls from motorists after they have passed through the tunnel. The ten lane southbound tunnel is located on the approach to the new Tyne Tunnel, collecting motorists' tolls before they enter the tunnel. The southbound plaza has the potential to operate as a bi-directional plaza, which was essential during the refurbishment of the older vehicle tunnel.

The Toll Plazas are capable of handling nearly 30 million vehicle transactions per year, and are designed to be fully automated to free up traffic flow.

A major objective set by TWITA was to keep tolls as low as possible, hence the most expensive design choices were not pursued during building the new tunnel. The toll in 1967 was two shillings and sixpence (12.5p) for cars, which equated to approximately £1.90 in 2011, when both tunnels came into use. The future toll projections, which are less than this, therefore represent good value compared to the original Tyne Tunnel toll.

NK60 EPF

Midnight Commissioning

At midnight on 25th February 2011 the new Tyne Tunnel welcomed its first passengers. Motorists queued on the A19 to be amongst the first to travel through the Tyne's newest vehicular river crossing in twenty years. Certificates were handed out to the first one hundred motorists, in celebration of the moment thousands of people had worked towards for more than a decade.

THE NEW

TYNE CROSSING

Friday 25th February 2011

Commemorating the commissioning of the new Tyne Tunnel

The holder of this certificate was amongst the first one hundred people to travel through the second Tyne vehicle tunnel upon its commissioning.

Cllr David Wood	Trevor Jackson	Nicolas Caille
Chairman of the Tyne and Wear Integrated Transport Authority	Managing Director TT2 Limited	Project Managing Director Bouygues Travaux Publics UK

TYNE AND WEAR INTEGRATED TRANSPORT AUTHORITY

BOUYGUES TRAVAUX PUBLICS

HISTORY

The first road tunnel

A new look for an old tunnel

Completion of the second Vehicle Tunnel was a major milestone in the New Tyne Crossing project. However, it represented only part of the £260 million scheme, designed to alleviate congestion at the UK's fourth worst traffic bottle neck and complete the dualling of the A19 corridor through the North East of England.

Despite the anticipation and excitement surrounding the commissioning of the second road tunnel, when the barriers lifted at the new toll plaza at midnight on 25 February 2011, the solution to traffic congestion had not been fully unveiled. It was only the first phase of the New Tyne Crossing scheme. As the new tunnel came into use the original, 1967-built road tunnel quietly closed. The aging toll barriers were lowered and days later the entire plaza had been entirely flattened as a major refurbishment programme was launched.

Two decades earlier the tunnel owners, the then Tyne and Wear Passenger Transport Authority (now TWITA), had contemplated how the heavily used road tunnel could be thoroughly overhauled. Safety standards were being met at the tunnel through use of additional specialised traffic staff and highly trained first responders on site. The intense safety management measures were necessary because by design the tunnel was no longer capable of meeting increasingly strict tunnel safety standards. International standards had been heightened following the tragic fire at the French-Italian Mont Blanc Tunnel in 1999.

The extent of the refurbishment works would require the tunnel to close to traffic for around a year. It was considered that closing the tunnel for such an extended period would create unacceptable disruption across Tyne and Wear. Hence the proposal to build a second road tunnel offered the additional advantage of providing an alternative route under the Tyne while the original tunnel closed for refurbishment.

Peter Hedley, previous Tyne Tunnel Manager, retired on the day the new Vehicle Tunnel came into operation. Having witnessed the development of the plans for the New Tyne Crossing, and managed tunnel operations during construction works, he felt a great sense of pride when the new tunnel accepted its first customers.

"Tunnels are really conduits that link places and people," he says. "They enable and facilitate, bringing people together and allowing access to leisure, opportunity, work and business. I've always thought that the Tyne Tunnels were the arteries of the community. It is maybe not surprising that the first Vehicle Tunnel became so popular, with demand outstripping capacity to such an extent. The Tyne Tunnels take people where they want to go."

Conceiving the first road tunnel

The need for a crossing of the River Tyne towards the river mouth was a long running aspiration. Since the 1800s designs for a river crossing between North and South Shields had been considered. Bridges presented design challenges due to the constraints imposed by the shipping traffic along the Tyne, yet nonetheless numerous designs were developed over the years. By the 1920s an engineer named F. W. Chalmers Kearney developed ambitious plans for an under river electric monorail for high speed rail cars, with a wider tunnel running alongside it for the transportation by rail of cars and buses. The

monorail route would link Tynemouth and South Shields, and the concept gained a Provisional Order in 1926 by the Ministry of Transport, enabling the system to be developed. The proposal faced local objections however, and the Bill was eventually rejected by the House of Commons.

Before the Tyne's first road tunnel came into existence motorists wishing to cross the river faced an inconvenient diversion via the bridges between Newcastle and Gateshead, some seven miles upstream, or travel via passenger and car ferry. A ferry service provided a dedicated transfer for vehicles between Jarrow and East Howdon from at least 1854 courtesy of the Tyne General Ferry Company. With ship building so prevalent on the Tyne a direct crossing point of the river was hugely advantageous, and the queue to board the ferry may well have been preferable to the detour via Newcastle and Gateshead. However neither option offered the instant convenience being demanded by contemporary society. Hence consideration of a more permanent, eastern river crossing became increasingly demanded.

Firming up plans for the Jarrow-Howdon river crossing

By 1937 the County Councils of Durham and Northumberland had developed a scheme to build three tunnels under the Tyne: a Pedestrian tunnel; a Cyclist tunnel; and a Vehicle tunnel. It was considered important that pedestrian and cyclist access could be facilitated by the river crossing, hence the clear commitment to a separate route for each group.

The onset of the Second World War then delayed the development of the Tyne Tunnels and plans were put on hold until 1946, by which time the estimated cost for the three tunnels was £3,600,000. In 1946 an act of Parliament called the 'Tyne Tunnel Act' was passed and this empowered the joint committee of the County Councils of Durham and Northumberland to go ahead and build the tunnels. However, lack of available funds meant that it was not possible to build all tunnels at once. Plans for the more expensive road tunnel were therefore put on hold, and the focus shifted onto the Pedestrian and Cyclist Tunnels, which opened in 1951.

The detailed plans for the vehicle tunnel had been

prepared and carried forward, but successive Government Transport Ministers declined to authorise the road tunnel's construction. By 1956 these delays had the effect of requiring a further piece of legislation to be passed by Parliament in order to extend the permitted timeline for the road tunnel's construction works, which had been stipulated under the original 1946 Act. The delays had also caused the estimated costs to rise to more than £12,000,000 by 1957.

The joint committee of the County Councils continued to press the Government to allow the project to be undertaken. In February of 1957 the Government Transport Secretary of the day announced that any new project of this type must partly pay for itself and that if it were to proceed the road tunnel must therefore be tolled. By the autumn of 1961 the plans, approvals and consents were all in place and construction of the Tyne Vehicle Tunnel commenced.

Building the original road tunnel

The original vehicular Tyne Tunnel is 1650 metres long, descending at a gradient of 1 in 20 (5%), to a maximum depth of just over 30 metres beneath the river water level. The lie of the land at the northern end of the tunnel required a steep climb up from the river bed. To make the climb back out of the tunnel easier for motorists it was therefore decided to introduce a winding section of road that enabled an easier ascent. This resulted in a shorter and more affordable tunnel than might otherwise have been required if the route had continued on a straight path.

The tunnel is lined throughout with cast iron segments, bolted together, and caulked with lead strip. Together, these features combine to create a tube with an internal diameter of 9.53 metres and capable of withstanding a water pressure of 310 kilo Pascals (just over 3 bar).

Despite requiring a variety of different tunnelling techniques, to accommodate the varying ground conditions, overall the first road tunnel was dug in a very conventional manner. The method could be compared to the excavation of a "face" in a coal mine.

Work began from the northern entrance. The first 275 metres mainly saw excavations into hard boulder clay, which was stable enough to stand in, and created a vertical face. The lower half of the face was dug out with a standard excavator that had been fitted with a demolition hook, rather than the usual bucket scoop.

Dump trucks continually removed the excavated waste material, and transported it off site along a temporary road within the tunnel space.

A cast of thousands (of tonnes)

Unlike the new Vehicle Tunnel, which reveals visibly different cross sections along its length due to the variety of tunnelling techniques used, in the original Vehicle Tunnel the profile remains the same throughout. This is thanks to the circular cast iron rings that were used to create the tunnel's shape, and hold the excavation in place. 45,000 tonnes of cast iron segments were used in the primary lining of the tunnel.

The cast iron rings were created in segments and transported along the tunnel by truck or bogie, where they would be lifted onto the gantry to be positioned into the excavated space. The segments were held in place while the bolts were inserted and tightened, although the water sealing grommets were not inserted until the entire unit had been set into position.

Under Pressure

In the damp section of the tunnel, on the approach to the river and beneath it, staff worked in compressed air in order to keep groundwater out of the work space, and to provide ground stability. The higher air pressure in the work space meant that water flowed away from that section rather than into it. Whilst creating a manageable work space, this also meant that the construction workers had to go through a decompression chamber as they left the tunnel workings, and restrictions were in place to protect workers from effects such as Decompression Sickness, or "the Bends".

An air lock was installed, which was managed by a 'Lock Keeper'. Amongst his duties, the Lock Keeper was responsible for carefully logging all staff that passed through the air lock, and subsequently decompressing them for the appropriate period of time.

Once tunnelling had progressed downhill from the glacial deposits, different tunnelling techniques had to be used. The most challenging conditions required the bedrock to be blasted with explosives in a carefully controlled manner that would not dislodge the unstable, softer ground conditions above. Blasting often released a steady flow of water which required ground injections to manage it. A 12 foot diameter pilot tunnel had been dug prior to the main tunnel, and beneath the river much of the ground injection treatment was carried out from the smaller tunnel.

The tunnel interior

Once the cast iron tunnel tube had been installed and caulked (made watertight), the gaps between the rings on the lower part of the tunnel were filled with concrete to form a secondary lining. With the main structure complete, it was then necessary to fit out the tunnel to create a suitable and roadworthy environment for motorists.

The construction of the road deck was carried out using pre-cast concrete units, each weighing 22 tonnes, and measuring 2.4 metres by 8 metres. The road deck was set down upon a bracket, creating a vacant space beneath the road that was 2.13 metres high at the centre point. This space beneath the road deck was used to distribute clean fresh air along the tunnel's length.

The road surface was created with hand laid mastic asphalt, four centimetres thick. The asphalt was heated outside the tunnel and transported in heated tankers to be laid inside the tunnel. This activity began from the south entrance of the tunnel, and took nine weeks to complete. The fumes from the asphalt were extracted by the permanent tunnel ventilation system. The central traffic lines were recessed into the asphalt, providing a 3.66 metre lane in each direction. There was a space of 5.2 metres above the road deck, which provided clearance for vehicles up to 4.87metres high through the tunnel up to the point of its refurbishment in 2011.

At the top of the tunnel, a false ceiling was formed from dark blue vitreous enamelled sheet panels, suspended from a steel roof frame with an asbestos cement drip shed above. The walls were lined with a secondary lining using off-white vitreous enamelled steel sheets, resulting in the familiar interior the original tunnel displayed for many years.

Fittings and features

The Vehicle Tunnel was fitted with all the necessary equipment and features to enable it to function efficiently, around the clock, every day of the year. Although maintenance work would be possible, and necessary, once the tunnel was operational, in order to minimise disruption to motorists it was vital that, as far as possible, the tunnel would run smoothly with minimal need for major operational maintenance or repair activities.

Pumps were located in the lowest point of the tunnel so that any drainage water could be pumped out and into a holding sump at the north side, ready to be pumped off site if suitable for release into the public drainage system. The drainage system was designed as a closed system in case a chemical spillage should occur inside the tunnel. If a substance was discharged into the sump that was unsuitable for wider release, it could be held until a specialist disposal firm was able to remove it safely.

As well as being essential for human safety, the tunnel was fitted with key emergency fire control features to help minimise the possible damage to the tunnel in the case of fire. Under normal circumstances fires are destructive, and can take lives. However the potential risks of fires within tunnels are elevated due to the immense temperatures they can reach in such confined spaces. Hence every 47metres, on the southbound side of the original Vehicle Tunnel, an emergency "fire point" had been installed. This contained an emergency phone that linked directly to the control room, as well as a 9 kg dry powder fire extinguisher, a hydrant on a 150mm fire main, and an automatic hose reel.

In an underground environment such as a road tunnel lighting is another vital consideration for the safe passage of motorists. In the original Vehicle Tunnel lighting levels were not only installed to meet the relevant safety standards, but just as importantly the lighting ensured that drivers were not subjected to sudden changes in the intensity of lighting as they entered or exited the tunnel. It was for the latter reason that a continuous line of fluorescent lighting was mounted on the ceiling at the centre line of the tunnel. This lighting was designed to be more intense near the entrances than in the mid-point of the tunnel. In addition shaded sun visors were provided at the tunnel entrances so that motorists could gradually adapt to the darker conditions within.

The Tunnel Chimneys

The provision of fresh air within a road tunnel is essential. In the original Vehicle Tunnel this was achieved using a system called semi transverse ventilation, with fresh air delivered equally along the tunnel's length and the exhaust fumes being drawn off at two specific points. Two ventilation stations were constructed, on either side of the river, to enable this type of ventilation to take place. Their conical, tiled chimney shafts have become local landmarks during the four decades in which they have served the Tyne Tunnel. The station in Jarrow served the main length of the tunnel, with the ventilation station on the north bank of the river serving the winding bend in the tunnel.

Each ventilation building featured a duty and a standby inlet fan which forced air down a shaft beneath the fan and into a ventilation duct beneath the road. Ventilation windows with removable vents

were set at kerb level along the length of the tunnel, enabling fresh air to be continuously pumped into the tunnel's interior. The hot exhaust fumes, meanwhile, rolled along the ceiling of the tunnel until they reached one of the two chimney shafts, where the exhaust fumes could be extracted. The 'Evasse' type chimneys stand at just over 46 metres high.

Tunnel Approach

The new approach roads were a separate part of the construction contract and their cost came to £1,000,000. Work on the tunnel approaches took place at the same time as the works to the tunnel interior. 'Open cut construction' at the southern entrance involved building a reinforced concrete slab as a retaining wall to hold open an excavated path into the ground. The tunnel approach continued nine metres below ground level, where it joined the main tunnel excavation.

At the northern entrance the approach includes a retaining wall and an open 'colonnade' or column-based structure, which uses the natural contours of the ground to create the best visual effect.

Regal Opening

The official opening of the first vehicular Tyne Tunnel by Her Majesty Queen Elizabeth II on 19th October 1967

THE grand opening of the first vehicular Tyne Tunnel was performed by Her Majesty The Queen, accompanied by His Royal Highness The Duke of Edinburgh, on Thursday 19th October 1967. This was an auspicious affair that involved many dignitaries including the Duchess of Northumberland, the Mayor & Mayoress of Newcastle and the Bishop of Newcastle, as well as politicians from the Counties of Durham and Northumberland.

On the northern side of the site there was a Guard of Honour provided by the 1st Battalion, The Royal Northumberland Fusiliers, with the Battalion's band and drums giving a Royal Salute. Her Majesty The Queen inspected the Guard of Honour.

The Lord Bishop of Newcastle dedicated the Tyne Tunnel in a religious service, after which The Queen declared the tunnel open. There then followed a 21 Gun Royal Salute, fired by a Battery of the Royal Artillery (Volunteers).

Her Majesty The Queen and His Royal Highness The Duke of Edinburgh then travelled by car through the toll plaza and tunnel to the southern junction. At the approaches to the tunnel entrances there were detachments of the Sea Cadet Corps, the Army Cadet Force, the Air Training Corps, the Girls' Venture Corps, Boy Scouts, Girl Guides, the Boys' Brigade and the Church Lads' Brigade.

At the southern end of the Tunnel The Queen inspected another Guard of Honour, this time provided by the 1st Battalion, The Durham Light Infantry, with The Queen's Colour and the Regimental Band and Bugles.

After two and a half hours at the Tyne Tunnel The Queen and The Duke of Edinburgh left site, to the accompaniment of a Royal Salute from the Guard of Honour, to join their Royal Train at Jarrow Railway Station. Despite the typical autumnal weather, crowds were out in force to witness the presence of the reigning Monarch in Jarrow and Howdon, with hundreds of flag-waving school children lining the streets to welcome the Royal couple. This two and a half hours of history resulted in a grand day that is still remembered in the North East with pride.

Refurbishing the original tunnel

THE 1999 fire in the Mont Blanc Road Tunnel was a very serious and fatal incident that led to new guidance and regulations being introduced for road tunnels that are located within the Trans European Road Network (TERN). The Tyne Tunnel does not form part of the TERN. However, the change in attitudes towards tunnel management following the Mont Blanc fire resulted in new Road Tunnel Safety Regulations being developed. The new design standards were included in the tender documents for the New Tyne Crossing project, which included the full refurbishment of the older Vehicle Tunnel. These new regulations were in addition to the already prescriptive United Kingdom Road Tunnel Design Standards. With the tunnel structure firmly set by its original cast iron rings, the requirements set by the new design standards would be challenging to achieve.

In a nutshell...

The overhaul of the original Vehicle Tunnel was intended to bring it up to modern safety and operational standards. Once complete the refurbished tunnel would provide two lanes for northbound traffic while the new tunnel would offer two lanes for southbound traffic.

The refurbishment works included demolition and removal of the inner tunnel lining, the road deck, the raised walkways, and all of the old services to the original tunnel. A new, pre-fabricated concrete wall was installed inside the tunnel to create an escape passage similar in function to the one in the new tunnel. The road drainage and utilities supplies were completely revised during the refurbishment as well, with the space beneath the road deck fitted out to accommodate the tunnel's utilities. By relocating the utilities beneath the road deck, space could be created for the escape passage above the road deck.

It was also possible to change the tunnel ventilation system due to the fact that all traffic would be travelling in the same direction, rather than bi-directionally, as previously. A new crash barrier was built onto the east tunnel wall to protect the primary tunnel lining, which was once protected from traffic impacts by the raised walkways.

An innovative solution

During the bidding process the successful tenderer, Bouygues TP, brought further innovation and engineering excellence to the design in terms of their approach towards meeting safety standards. On behalf of the Bouygues-led consortium engineering consultants Parsons Brinckerhoff developed the concept of an escape passage built within the envelope of the existing tunnel.

"The original reference design had sought to install two discrete vertical escape shafts within what would become the northbound road tunnel." explains Dr Alan Common, the Parsons Brinckerhoff Design Manager. "In the event of an emergency incident in the tunnel, motorists would be expected to escape from the tunnel via the two emergency exit shafts leading up to the surface. We had a better idea that we could create a dedicated safety escape passage running alongside the entire length of the road tunnel. This gave extra safety in the event of a fire, enabling motorists to safely leave the tunnel along a continuous protected escape corridor accessible from numerous emergency exits, rather than needing to be reached by only one of two exits. It gave the refurbished tunnel the equivalent safety standard as the new tunnel and is the first European tunnel to be refurbished this way."

The added advantage of this design was that the tunnel operator would be able to use the same safety and management procedures for both tunnels, rather than requiring totally different procedures for each. This similarity in safety management systems further enhances the safety of the measures in place, leaving less opportunity for confusion and error.

In order to achieve this revised design, it was necessary to realign the road lanes within the tunnel, to create the necessary space for the new escape passage. The raised, open walk ways that had previously run along the length of the tunnel would need to be removed, leaving the traffic lanes to run directly adjacent to the tunnel walls. Due to the curve of the tunnel ceiling, this therefore would leave one lane with height restrictions, the curve of the ceiling making the outer lane unsuitable for high sided vehicles.

Making way for improvements

The first stages of the older tunnel's facelift actually began before the new tunnel had become operational, and while live traffic continued to use the original bi-directional route.

In order to gain a clearer understanding of the condition of the original tunnel structure, Bouygues Travaux Publics began removing the enamelled panels from the tunnel walls. This allowed the original cast iron segments, their bolts, and the waterproof caulking to be closely examined.

Fortunately these preliminary investigations did not reveal any faults or issues of concern. As soon as the new tunnel became operational, and traffic transferred across into the new route, the older tunnel was closed, as was the control room that had served it for more than forty years, and both quickly faced the firm hand of demolition.

Within days of closing the old toll plaza had been razed to the ground, along with the tunnel portals and the raised walk ways within the tunnel. The control room underwent a gradual transformation into new office space, with all control functions for both tunnels being provided from the new control room that was already serving the new Vehicle Tunnel.

DID YOU KNOW?....

The ceiling of the original road tunnel contained

asbestos, which had to be removed in a strictly controlled manner. Once removed and stored, ready to be sent to a licensed disposal site, the waste had to be transported across the Tyne via an alternative route, due the stringent controls in place at the Tyne Tunnels regarding the type of materials that may or may not be carried through the tunnels. Ironically, even though the asbestos had originated within the tunnel, it could not be transported through it to be taken to its disposal site.

Transforming safety

The original road tunnel was once rated as one of the least safe tunnels in Europe. While the safety management systems were praised, and acknowledged as keeping the site safe, the structure itself was criticised. The outdated structure and facilities ranked very poorly against other road tunnels, and only the excellent management procedures and staffing maintained the tunnel's good safety record.

The tunnel's refurbishment saw the total transformation of the safety standards at the site. Emergency doors in both tunnels give access to dedicated escape passages, wide enough to accommodate wheelchair users or people on stretchers, and separate from the main vehicle route to provide protection from fumes and high temperatures. Exit doors are located every 100 metres, so that in the case of an emergency no-one would need to walk more than 50m to the nearest exit. Illuminated signage indicates the closest escape exit, and once inside the escape passage further signage indicates the nearest tunnel exit.

The escape passages in both tunnels are specially designed to trigger an increase in air pressure if the escape doors are opened. The higher air pressure inside the escape passage pushes smoke or fumes out of the escape passage, and prevents smoke from entering the passageway. This keeps the air fresh within the escape passage for people to safely leave the tunnel.

When designing safety into a structure such as a road tunnel it is important not only to consider the safety of people in the tunnel, but also the structural integrity of the tunnel itself. During the refurbishment of the original Vehicle Tunnel the tunnel structure was protected from potential fire damage in two ways: with new concrete, thick enough to withstand very hot, intense fires, or with a type of fire protection board called "Promat Board". These measures provide in-built resistance. In addition to this the tunnel was also fitted with a Fixed Fire Suppression System, of exactly the same specification as had been installed in the new Vehicle Tunnel. The Tyne Tunnels were the first in the UK to benefit from these intense mist safety systems, requiring Tyne and Wear Fire and Rescue Service to work with colleagues to develop the safety response standard from scratch.

An emergency exercise was held in the refurbished tunnel before it was recommissioned for use. The exercise tested the response of all emergency services as well as the Tyne Tunnel's operation staff, to a mock emergency incident. With new safety systems in place it was vital that the responses of all key people and procedures could be properly assessed. The mock incident involved a fake chemical spill, and resulted in the sprinkler system being activated once the chemical involved had been ascertained. The event demonstrated that the tunnels would operate more safely than ever before with their new safety features.

More than just a hole in the ground

There is a lot more to both vehicle tunnels than meets the eye. The tunnels are fitted with a huge number of technical and safety features, all designed to help people pass easily and safely beneath the Tyne.

In the older Vehicle Tunnel, twenty two new jet fans were fitted to the tunnel's roof to enable "Longitudinal" ventilation to provide the fresh air within the tunnel. The longitudinal ventilation differs from the original approach to ventilating the tunnel when it operated bi-directionally. The new system allows the mechanical ventilation to work in harmony with the air movements within the tunnel caused by the traffic flow. With all traffic flowing in the same direction the longitudinal ventilation system enhances the natural flow of air. The ventilation system also works to support the Fixed Fire Suppression System, (the mist system), to prevent a fire growing or spreading to other vehicles.

The ventilation fans in both tunnels have the potential to move air at 22 miles per hour. This is akin to a Force 5 wind if measured on the Beaufort Scale (a fresh breeze that could develop a 6 to 9 foot swell

at sea, move moderate size branches on a tree, or make small trees sway).

The older tunnel has also been fitted with 56 closed circuit television cameras along its length, as opposed to the 32 cameras in the new tunnel. The greater number of cameras in the older tunnel enables full coverage of the winding bend at the northern end of the tunnel.

As with the new Vehicle Tunnel, the refurbished tunnel also benefits from a public address system, Variable Message Signs, a radio break-in system that allows the control room to send messages via a driver's own vehicle radio, as well as the illuminated evacuation signs that indicate the closest exits from the tunnel. These communication channels support the full range of safety equipment that is installed throughout both tunnels.

The tunnel was also fitted out with new lighting, installed to meet UK and European Lighting Standards. The lighting introduced to both vehicle tunnels has the added benefit of being more environmental friendly than the original fluorescent lighting system previously installed in the older Vehicle Tunnel.

1,189 lights have been installed to light the road tunnels (573 light fittings in the new tunnel and 616 light fittings in the original tunnel).

DID YOU KNOW?....

184 kilometres of power cables and 118 kilometres of fibre optics have been fitted to the tunnels as part of the New Tyne Crossing project - if laid end to end the cables would stretch from the Tyne Tunnels to beyond the Mersey Tunnels in Liverpool.

For the drainage system a total of 29 kilometres of pipework was installed (13.8 kilometres in the new tunnel and 15.2 kilometres during the refurbishment of the original tunnel). Laid end to end the pipes would stretch from the tunnels to beyond Hexham in Northumberland.

Returning the Portals to the Public

Above the tunnel portal in Jarrow a lightweight polystyrene fill has replaced the sun visor. This provides a secure foundation to enable the land above the tunnel to be used for public enjoyment, for the first time in the tunnels' history, without creating

020-8646 4466

an unacceptably heavy load upon the tunnel structure. There are strict planning controls for land use above the tunnel, so that no buildings can be constructed above the tunnel portal, and only minimal planting may take place. Nonetheless, despite these restrictions, the benefits of the open space for public enjoyment are greatly appreciated locally.

The commitment to create this area as public space arose as a result of the loss of open space in front of Epinay Walk, to make way for the new loop road at the south junction.

Keeping things on track

Bouygues Travaux Publics made excellent progress towards completing the tunnel refurbishment by carrying out works simultaneously at both ends of the tunnels. Demolition of the tunnel interiors was undertaken at the same time, at the northern and southern ends of the tunnel, with a one way traffic system in place so that all construction vehicles would enter the tunnel work space from the north, and exit at the south.

Once demolitions had progressed a suitable distance, tracks were laid that would allow the pre-cast concrete wall units to be easily rolled into place inside the tunnel. These units would make up the new escape passage for the original Vehicle Tunnel. A continually rolling programme of works ensured that no time was wasted during the refurbishment of what would become the northbound Vehicle Tunnel.

To ensure the works were built in accordance with the strict requirements of the project and to relevant standards and guidance, a number of bodies were responsible for inspecting, reviewing and monitoring the development of the design and the progress of the works on site.

TT2 employed an 'in-house' construction manager and TWITA retained Arup as technical advisor throughout the construction stage of the project to look after their interests. In addition, an Independent Certifier was appointed to oversee the process to ensure the tunnels were safe to be opened to the public.

Arup's Malcolm Shaw explains his team's role in the project "Our client, TWITA, wished to obtain a high quality product in a safe manner and to do so with consideration for all stakeholders including local communities and the travelling public. To realise this, our technical team was integrated into the client project management team based on site; to review design information, to monitor the delivery of the construction works and to assist in ensuring compliance with the relevant contract standards. The Arup team was supported by colleagues based in Newcastle and other specialists in the UK and worldwide.

"The successful completion of the works, on time, came as a result of working collaboratively with TT2, Bouygues, the Independent Certifier, North and South Tyneside Councils, the Highways Agency and other stakeholders to ensure that the necessary approvals and consents were provided in a timely manner".

The close liaison between all the parties ensured that there were no surprises during delivery. This integrated approach enabled the tunnels to be opened ahead of the planned date.

Transformation Complete: The life changing Tyne Tunnels

On 21st November 2011 the original road tunnel re-opened to traffic after nine months of intense efforts to transform it. Not only was there a physical transformation within the tunnel, which now operated as a one way tunnel providing a route for northbound traffic only, but there was a wider transformation that also took place on 21st November.

From the moment that two vehicle tunnels became available to traffic the vision of the New Tyne Crossing project was realised. The notorious traffic jams that had plagued the route for so many years disappeared instantly. Onlookers suspected that traffic numbers must have dropped due to the apparent absence of vehicles approaching the tunnels during rush hour. However by the second day traffic numbers had risen by almost 5%, the vastly increased tunnel capacity handling the extra throughflow with ease.

Rachel Turnbull, Chief Executive Officer at TT2, said "I don't think anyone expected traffic to flow quite as freely as it does now that there are two tunnels available. A year on, we're still not seeing queues, even during peak hours. This is a project that really has made a difference to peoples' lives, and continues to do so. People tell us the tunnels

have changed their lives. What an incredible achievement for what is essentially just a short stretch of road."

TT2 was deluged with positive feedback after the two tunnels came into use. Motorists described the invaluable experiences the tunnels had allowed them to enjoy: the mother who for the first time was able to take her daughter to her after school dance lessons; the father able to get home in time to bathe his son before bedtime; the business owner estimating a doubling in turnover within six months thanks to the new markets that had been opened up by the free flowing tunnels.

One gentleman contacted TT2 to explain that he estimated he would save around six days a year, once spent sitting in traffic at the Tyne Tunnel. He had decided to pledge this extra time to charitable work.

As legacies go, the New Tyne Crossing has delivered myriad achievements: the engineering innovations, the environmental performance, the completion ahead of schedule, the efforts to minimise disruption during construction, the commitments to involving local communities, and the quality of life impacts for motorists and local people, to name but a few.

With the planned refurbishment of the Pedestrian and Cyclist Tunnels in 2013, the Tyne Tunnels have not only secured their place in history, but look set to remain a landmark site for the people of the North East for many more years to come.

CARRON

5.1 m MAXIMUM HEADROOM
LINE MARKING

51m MAXIMUM HEADROOM

Keith Hann
Page 19

...the new Tyne Tunnel

The new tunnel under the Tyne was expected to ease congestion on the A19. But since it opened, that's only been the start of its achievements. KATE PROCTOR reports

LIFE changing. A miracle. Amazing. It's hard to believe such words could be uttered about a concrete tunnel snaking its way under the River Tyne.

But thousands of commuters journeying twice-daily through the new Tyne Tunnel find their quality of life has improved more than the most optimistic engineers could have anticipated.

Time previously lost to traffic jams is now spent with family and friends. One man even uses his new-found hours to devote himself to charity work.

"The amount of people who say 'it's amazing' as if they are talking about some new invention is incredible," says commuter Rob Cox of Fellgate in Jarrow.

"It's as if we've all forgotten we're actually talking about a tunnel, but since it opened life has been so much better."

The YMCA chief executive works in Ashington and crosses the Tyne through the tunnel every day to get to work.

But like 45,000 other commuters, the opening of the new tunnel in November 2011 has chopped hours off his weekly drive to work.

"Before it was put in, it was a minimum of a 45-minute journey one way. Sometimes it could take one hour and 30 minutes just to travel 21 miles and to do that every day over three years was just soul destroying," said Rob, 30.

"Now I get in from work and actually have time to sit down and have dinner with my wife who is a teacher. There's no more eating on my own.

"We have our evenings back and it's just been incredible. You couldn't have predicted all that from just a bit of building work."

The new tunnel, which links Wallsend in North Tyneside to Jarrow in South Tyneside, opened 13 months ago. The original tunnel then closed for refurbishment. Both tunnels opened together in November 2011.

The thinking behind the £260m scheme was that a new toll tunnel would reduce the daily queues through the old single lane crossing, and make the A19 a continuous two-lane road.

The original Grade II listed tunnel, built in 1967, could cater for 20,000 vehicles a day when it was first built.

But as traffic numbers more than doubled, long queues to get across the river had, frustratingly, be-

Turn to 18>>

From «17

come an accepted part of people's daily lives. Rob said what should have been a routine commute to work was something that was never easy to predict.

"The wait itself was a really boring thing. It was time that was wasted and sometimes the other commuters didn't understand vehicles were intended to merge in turn [into the single lane as they approached the tunnel].

"Some people found it relaxing being in a queue, but for me it had the opposite effect. Lots of people were abusive and gestures were always flying through windows."

In 2004, permission was granted for work to start on a new tunnel, with consortium Tyne Tunnel 2 (TT2) appointed in November 2007 to build, design and part fund the scheme and operate both tunnels until 2037.

A year later 10,000 tonnes of concrete were floated down the Tyne to be laid on the river bed, 40ft below the surface.

The four pre-fabricated tunnel units, 90m long, were manoeuvred out of a dry dock at Walker and fused together in 2010.

Traffic was then switched to the new tunnel while the old was one refurbished over 10 months before, on November 21, both were opened to traffic to allow for a bidirectional two-lane tunnel system.

Social worker Scott Woodhouse, who works for North Tyneside council, spent three years in queues that he said robbed him of two hours every day.

"The first morning when the new tunnel opened, I went in early and was expecting the usual queue. I didn't think it would have made any difference, but there was nothing on the road.

It was like somebody flipping a switch. It was like a miracle."

His shorter journey times have helped him get home to South Shields earlier and spend more time with his wife and children Matthew, 20 and Kate, 17.

The 47-year-old said: "It's given me a better home life and personal life. Far better than spending two hours a day sat in a car.

"I did three years of the tunnel commute. It was a good move for my career to be on that side of the river, but the downside was the tunnel.

"My wife also notices the improvement. It's that flexibility. I can now arrange to do something and be able to do it at a certain time. I can also drop my wife off at work now and pick her up and if I say I'm going to be there for a certain time I will be."

But it's not only about getting home earlier. Productivity in the workplace has also been a helpful by-product of the new route.

For Rob Cox, this means he can now get to charity board meetings held after work throughout the North East, that help further his work for the YMCA. "I finish work at 5pm, but sometimes would need to leave early because I would have a board meeting for something to do with the YMCA. That's the nature of the job.

"Now I can get to the things I need to on time. I can do more of the community things I couldn't do before and I don't have to miss anything."

But for others, simple sleep is at the heart of the tunnel's main impact.

Karen Morgan, business adviser for mobile phone customer services company Everything Everywhere, based at Cobalt Business Park in North Tyneside, said: "I cannot emphasise the difference of coming to work in the mornings, after spending two years of travelling through what I can only describe as a living nightmare while they were building the new one. I had to get up one hour earli just to spend time sitting in a queu crawling along and barely getting out first gear.

"But that was then and this is now. I ca sleep an extra 45 minutes and we all li an extra few minutes in bed.

"I am no longer wondering if I w make it to work in time, I am no long frustrated before I get to work."

Businesses north and south of the riv have also noticed improvements in cruitment and the potential for ne markets since the tunnel opened.

South Tyneside councillor Jim Per lead member for neighbourhoods ar environment, believes the new crossir has the potential to bring econom growth to the region.

"There were a lot of concerns from loc residents about the mess and disruptic such a large engineering project mig cause, but I have to say that these fea were soon allayed because the proje was delivered," he said.

"The crossing will make a major co tribution to the work we are doing create the conditions needed to enab industry to thrive. The dramatic redu tion in congestion at each end of t crossing is not only benefiting the e vironment, but also providing our r idents with easier access to job oppo tunities along the A19 corridor."

That sentiment is echoed at Nor Tyneside's Cobalt Office Park which h 10,000 staff working from the site.

Directors there believe the new tunn has contributed to an increase in the recruitment from south of the river.

Adrian Hill, director of Highbridg Properties which owns the park, sai "The immediate feedback from our te ants is that the new tunnel has so si nificantly improved journey times f staff living in South Tyneside, that th are expecting to dramatically increase t ability to recruit in the area."

LIFE CHANGER
Above, the southside entrance to the new tunnel under the Tyne. Below, Rob and Katie Cox, from Jarrow, who have been delighted with the improved quality of life they've enjoyed since the new crossing opened

PAINTER GETS TO HEART OF THE TUNNEL PROJECT

EVERY twist and turn of the momentous project to build the new tunnel under the River Tyne was captured by Sunderland based artist Robert Soden.

The artist positioned himself to record the visual might of the engineering project as it unfolded.

From his eventual 35 paintings, six were chosen to mark the project's completion and they went on display in December at South Shields Museum and Art Gallery.

"It was a sublime experience, a mixture of awe and fear, excitement and trepidation," Robert said. "I could never forget that a great mass of water lay just behind the tunnel transition wall.

"I have worked a lot on building sites before and everybody is incredibly safety conscious.

"I painted directly on site and made sure I kept out of the way. They got used to me and I just blended in.

"I think they enjoyed seeing me paint what they were doing and valuing their work."

Robert's aim was to document the extent of work hidden from the gaze of the public.

"Most people were stuck in the traffic jams and a lot of the tunnel work went unseen. There was tremendous activity going on.

"What impressed me was the sheer scale of skills and trades which were all happening in a confined, concentrated area. It was fascinating."

Also lending her artistic talent to the project was North East mural painter Lynda Nelson.

She transformed three 6ft-wide marine buoys with decorative paintings and they were placed at the North Tyneside end of the tunnel as a welcoming gateway for commuters.

Lynda, who lives in Jarrow, was inspired by old railway posters used to entice people to destinations.

She said: "I am really happy with the way the buoys have turned out and how it has gone from small, original drawings to something so big. They should serve as a good introduction to North Tyneside and all it has to offer.

"It is amazing to think how many people will see them and I hope they'll be enjoyed for years to come."

The £15,000 art scheme was jointly funded by North Tyneside Council and Tyne Tunnel operator TT2.

PROJECT UNDER WAY The construction of the new tunnel through the eyes of artist Robert Soden

A 'Shields' river crossing

THE Tyne Pedestrian and Cyclist Tunnels were built to service the Industrial communities on either side of the River Tyne. At a time when industrial activity was vibrant along the banks of the river, providing the first dedicated tunnels to serve the area was seen a huge vote of confidence in the area. When the tunnels opened, in 1951, thousands of people used them every day.

The idea to build a tunnel crossing under the Tyne, to link the areas of North and South Shields, was born many years before the first tunnel appeared. In 1937, the Durham and Northumberland County Councils put forward a scheme for a road tunnel under the river between Howdon and Jarrow. Their plan was eventually approved and the Councils went on to promote the necessary Bill, which received the Royal Assent as the Tyne Tunnel Act, 1946.

This Act provided for the construction of a vehicular tunnel and two smaller tunnels, one 12 ft. wide and the other 10 ft. 6 in. wide for the use of cyclists and pedestrians respectively. Responsibility for implementing the project was placed with the Tyne Tunnel Joint Committee consisting of representatives of the two County Councils.

In 1946 the Ministry of Transport agreed to make a 75 per cent grant towards the construction costs of the tunnels, leaving the remaining costs to be met by the two Counties in equal shares. However, restrictions on capital expenditure were introduced in 1947, so that the the then Minister, the Right Hon. Alfred Barnes M.P., ruled that work on the Tyne Tunnels should initially focus solely on the pedestrian and cycle tunnels. The work of driving these tunnels began in June 1947.

An average of 17,000 people travelled through the tunnels each day to get to work, before the Vehicle Tunnel opened, peaking at 20,000. The rise in car use and the steady decline of industry, especially shipbuilding, greatly reduced the usage of the tunnels, which had been perfectly situated to support the riverbank industries. Today, there are around 20,000 journeys through the tunnels every month, rather than every day. However, in recent years the downward trend has begun to reverse as cycling increases in popularity, both for commuters and for leisure users.

The tunnels were constructed to the designs of Durham and Northumberland County Councils' Engineers Departments. The Civil Engineering Contractor was Charles Brand & Son Ltd of London under the supervision of Dr (later Sir) David Anderson of Mott, Hay & Anderson, consulting civil engineers, of London.

Work on the Pedestrian and Cyclist Tunnels commenced in June 1947 and was completed in July 1951 at a cost of £900,000 for both of the tunnels.

A great deal was learned about the geological conditions during the construction of these first tunnels, which went on to inform plans for the eventual construction of the first road tunnel.

Inside the tunnels

The tunnels are just over 232 metres long, and share the same entrance halls.. The Pedestrian Tunnel is 3.2 metres in diameter and the Cyclist Tunnel is 3.65 metres in diameter, providing extra space for those mounted on bicycles.

The distinctive pale green and yellow ceramic tiling that features along the length of both tunnels was supplied by Carter & Co, in Poole, which became part of Pilkington Tiles in 1964

DID YOU KNOW?....

At the centre of the tunnels there are tiled signs to indicate the middle of the river. You can stand with one foot in the 'COUNTY OF NORTHUMBERLAND' and the other in the 'COUNTY OF DURHAM'.

The tunnels were equipped with wooden escalators and a passenger lift at either end. Following the model of St Anna Tunnel in Antwerp (built between 1931-3), engineers used a similar system of connecting the tunnels to their surface buildings via two escalators and a lift at either end. This was unlike earlier tunnels such as Greenwich (1902) and Woolwich (1912) which relied on steps and lifts to provide access.

The Tyne Tunnels are the only pedestrian tunnels beneath a river to be fitted with escalators, and those in the cyclist tunnel were the first designed especially for cyclists, incorporating special safety features.

PEDESTRIANS TUNNEL
CYCLISTS TUNNEL

The world famous Tyne Tunnel escalators

The four escalators within the Pedestrian and Cyclist Tunnels have been in place since the tunnels opened in 1951. They were produced by Waygood-Otis. Each has 306 wooden steps and were the same type as installed in the London Underground. The King's Cross Fire of 1987 led to the decision to install a fire sprinkler system above the Tyne Tunnel escalators.

The wooden escalators are 61 metres long and their vertical rise is 26 metres. They were the first in the country to be used by cyclists as well as pedestrians, and for many years these escalators were cited in the Guinness Book of Records as being the longest single span wooden escalators in the world.

Celebrating Progress

The Tyne Pedestrian and Cyclist Tunnels were opened by Alfred Barnes, Minister of Transport, on 24th July 1951. They were promoted as Tyneside's contribution to the Festival of Britain. There are similarities between the reinforced concrete roofs of the Rotunda (entrance) buildings and that of the main pavilion at the Festival of Britain, the Dome of Discovery.

At their opening, the tunnels were the longest subterranean passages and the first purpose-built cycle tunnel in the UK. They were also the first to be designed for both cyclists and pedestrians.

Today they remain as one of only four purpose built pedestrian tunnels under rivers that are still operating in the UK.

The tunnels, which are currently owned and managed by the Tyne & Wear Integrated Transport Authority (TWITA), celebrated their Diamond Jubilee in 2011.

Architectural Interest

The special interest of the tunnels was recognised in May 2000 when they were added to the Statutory List of Buildings of Special Architectural or Historic Interest at Grade II. The listing assessment took account of the many aspects of the tunnels' interest including their post-war municipal design, use of materials and detailing, the intactness of the complex including the survival of the four rare Waygood-Otis

CYCLISTS
TUNNEL

wooden escalators, and their historic interest as the first purpose-built combined pedestrian and cycle tunnels in the United Kingdom, which also constituted the area's contribution to the 1951 Festival of Britain.

An exciting future for the oldest Tyne Tunnels

TWITA has implemented an improvement plan at the Tyne Pedestrian and Cyclist Tunnels since 2010, when the two vertical lifts were refurbished. It was at that time that TWITA also announced its intention to invest £6 million on a major overhaul of the tunnels.

The planned upgrade of the sixty year old tunnels will feature the replacement of two of the wooden escalators with inclined lifts. The other two escalators will be preserved for people to visit. They will no longer be operational but visitors to the tunnels will be able to see the workings of the escalators, while traveling in the new inclined lifts. Work on the refurbishment is expected to begin in 2013.

B

A Gem of a Royal Opening

THE second vehicular Tyne Tunnel was officially opened by Her Majesty The Queen forty five years after she opened the Tyne's first road tunnel in October 1967, during her Diamond Jubilee tour of the region.

Accompanied by His Royal Highness The Duke of Edinburgh, The Queen began her visit at the Jarrow junction of the Tyne Tunnels, in South Tyneside.

She began her visit by starting a showcase run of the annual Tyne Tunnel 2k Wheelchair Race. Three of the regular T2K competitors took part in the special Jubilee race, which was won by Great Britain's Paralympian, 21 year old Mickey Bushell. Also competing were local athletes Jade Jones and Simon Lawson, both of whom are coached by Baroness Tanni Grey Thompson and her husband Dr. Ian Thompson.

Whilst the wheelchair athletes sprinted through the northbound (refurbished) Tyne Tunnel towards the finish line in Howdon, Her Majesty The Queen and His Royal Highness The Duke of Edinburgh met the Mayor and Mayoress of South Tyneside and the Chief Executive of South Tyneside Council, as well as representatives from the organisations behind the £260M New Tyne Crossing.

Councillor Eileen Leask, Mayor of South Tyneside, announced "It was a great honour to welcome Her Majesty to our borough, and wonderful to see so many local people providing a warm South Tyneside welcome. It was fantastic to have The Queen to officially open the tunnel that has made such a difference to people's lives, especially as Her Majesty opened the first tunnel 45 years ago".

The Royal visitors were escorted during their visit by Mr Trevor Jackson, Managing Director of TT2, and Mr Barry Rowland, Clerk of the Tyne and Wear Integrated Transport Authority.

Whilst in Jarrow The Queen met members of the local community from both South and North Tyneside who were actively involved in supporting their

GIRO
CORIMA

neighbours through the construction works.

The Duke of Edinburgh met representatives from Bouygues Travaux Publics, the main Design and Build contractor. Mr Nicolas Caille, the Project Director, introduced staff from across the organisation with the Chairman of the Bouygues Group, Mr Martin Bouygues, also present to meet the Royal Party.

Mr Caille said "I am incredibly proud to see Her Majesty officially open the new tunnel. Thousands of people were involved in its construction, and it is a wonderful feeling to have our work recognised by The Queen".

Before departing from Jarrow, Her Majesty was invited to plant a commemorative oak tree. It forms part of The Queen's Jubilee Wood, which aims to plant 6 million native trees across Britain. The oak tree is recorded in the Royal Record of Trees, established to commemorate the Queen's Diamond Jubilee.

The Royal Party travelled through the new Vehicle Tunnel to the southbound toll plaza north of the Tyne, where they were greeted by the Longbenton RAF Squadron Band. After meeting the Chairman of North Tyneside Council and his consort, the Chief Executive of North Tyneside Council and North Tyneside MP Mrs Mary Glindon, the Royal Party then congratulated the wheelchair athletes, who had completed their race at the toll plaza.

The Elected Mayor of North Tyneside, Mrs. Linda Arkley, was also presented to Her Majesty The Queen. She said: "It was a great honour to welcome The Queen and Prince Philip to North Tyneside for the official opening of the new Tyne Tunnel. The tunnel has opened up so many improved opportunities for the people of North Tyneside, and beyond, that it truly has transformed peoples' lives. It is a fitting tribute that the second tunnel should be opened by Her Majesty".

During her visit to the Howdon Toll Plaza north of the Tyne Tunnels, The Queen was introduced to a group of TT2 staff, with Mr. Leslie Tennant, the then Chairman of TT2, present to welcome the Royal Party to the Tyne Tunnels.

Trevor Jackson, TT2's Managing Director, said "It was an incredible experience to host a visit by Her Majesty The Queen and The Duke of Edinburgh. We were delighted that The Queen chose to say a few words about the Tyne Tunnels and we feel honoured that she has recognised the achievements the project has made".

The Queen was also introduced to representatives from TWITA, the Project Promoter.

Mr Paul Fenwick, TWITA's Project Director, introduced some of those at the heart of the Transport Authority's project team, which spanned a lifetime of more than 15 years. Councillor David Wood, Chairman of TWITA, greeted the Royal party upon their arrival, commenting afterwards

"I have been lucky enough to witness history in the making on more than one occasion during this project, from the lowering of the river tunnel sections into the river bed, to driving through the new tunnel at its midnight commissioning. But to be present today at the official opening of the new tunnel by Her Majesty The Queen is something I will never forget. The New Tyne Crossing project has changed the lives of so many motorists and local people. It certainly is a project we can be proud of".

Perfect Posies

The Queen was presented with a hand tied posy of cream flowers before leaving both sides of the Tyne Tunnels.

Giselle Greulich-Smith, aged 12, offered Her Majesty a posy before the Royal Party left the Jarrow junction of the tunnels in South Tyneside.

On the north side of the river, The Queen was presented with a posy of flowers from North Tyneside school girl Lily Turnbull, aged 6. Both girls' mothers were closely involved in the delivery of the project.

THE NEW
TYNE CROSSING

The Queen's Speech at the opening of Tyne Tunnel Two

FORTY five years after I came here to open the first road tunnel under the River Tyne, Prince Philip and I are delighted to return for the official opening of Tyne Tunnel Two.

I know that the first tunnel has made a huge difference to people's lives in Tyneside, opening up access for many communities once so divided by this great river.

As car ownership increased, the need for a second tunnel became clear. After some four years of construction, using the latest technology, the highest standards of safety and a commendable attention to the needs of surrounding neighbourhoods, both tunnels opened to vehicles last November. And the task of relieving the congestion of traffic in Newcastle and Gateshead has undoubtedly been achieved, giving a better quality of life to residdents, businesses and commuters. Time once lost to traffic james can now be spent with family and friends.

Now the project is complete, I would like to congratulate all those who have played a part: the planners, the financiers, the engineers and contractors: everyone who has contributed to this great achievement of immense benefit to the North East region.

You can all be proud of a job well done.

I now have pleasure in declaring open Tyne Tunnel Two."

P108.

A trip down memory lane via The Tyne Tunnels

HUNDREDS of fascinating site tours took place during the delivery of the New Tyne Crossing project. Amongst them some very special visits stood out. These featured a small group of people from the thousands who had been involved in building the first road tunnel during the 1960s.

Senior Civil Engineer with Mott Hay and Anderson during the building of the original tunnel, Colin Blythman had visited the new Vehicle Tunnel when it was merely a muddy trench deep below the ground. Colin was able to visit the new Tyne Tunnel on several occasions during its construction, culminating in a visit with ex-colleagues shortly before the new river crossing opened to traffic in February 2011.

Amongst the guests visiting the new Vehicle Tunnel was Brenda Hutchison, who worked in the drawings office of the design team for the original Vehicle Tunnel. Brenda remembers "Women weren't allowed into the tunnel when it was being built, as it was considered bad luck. We were only allowed as far as the decompression chamber, which was interesting, but it was fascinating to look behind the scenes at the new tunnel – and to be allowed all the way on to the site!"

Peter Heenan was Lead Miner for five years during construction of the original tunnel, which opened in 1967, and remembers missing Christmas one year for the tunnel. "I went into the tunnel one Christmas morning with a colleague to carry out a face inspection" he recalled during his visit. "About 400ft into the tunnel we could see water glistening ahead. We knew we had to get the water out, and away from the electrics, so we started trying to clear it. Because we were working under compressed air, we could only stay down there for ten minutes at a time before coming back to the surface. So the process took longer than expected. I was meant to collect my father for Christmas dinner that morning, but when we didn't appear my wife thought I'd stopped off at the pub and stayed there all day! The tunnel really took over our lives."

Later that year a special visit was organised for those original tunnel workers, to show them what had been done during the refurbishment of the tunnel they had helped to create more than 40 years earlier.

Siltbuster
groundforce
shorco
Freephone
BOUYGUES
TRAVAUX PUBLICS

Local enterprise

CONSTRUCTION of the second Vehicle Tunnel and the refurbishment of the original was completed ahead of schedule and with minimum disruption thanks to the skills and hard work of its mainly North East workforce. Of the roughly 3500 people who were involved in building the new tunnel, almost 90% were from the North East. This excellent achievement in terms of local involvement was the result of a range of measures designed to maximise opportunities for local job hunters and businesses, without preventing those from further afield from taking up positions.

A Code of Local Procurement and Employment was developed by Bouygues Travaux Publics and contractor wood holmes at the start of the project to promote the use of local labour and a local supply chain. Although it was a voluntary code of practice, all sub-contractors signed up to it, and were actively encouraged to make the most of the opportunities for local involvement in the once in a lifetime scheme.

South Shields born Christine Smith was one of the people helping to make the project happen. Having worked for 8 years as an estate agent, Christine was made redundant. Through Job Smart in South Tyneside she was able to find work as assistant to the construction section managers and engineers, based at the site offices in Jarrow. Christine loved the challenge of her role, and the excitement of being involved in such a momentous project. She took up her post in September 2008, and was there to see both tunnels come into use on 21st November 2011. She says "I was apprehensive at first, but it didn't take long to settle in. Previously I was always customer facing, but at Bouygues I was more in the background, making sure everything was right and concentrating on internal servicing".

Andrew Wilkinson from Jarrow was appointed as Bouygues Travaux Public's Health and Safety Advisor in 2008, having previously worked on a range of high profile sites, including Sellafield in Cumbria. Andrew managed the site safety induction talks, which every person working on site had to attend. He also helped to enforce the Code of Construction Practice. "I really enjoyed seeing this project come together" reflects Andrew. "Some of the technology and techniques that were used were new and innovative, which presented a challenge from a professional perspective, but on a personal level it was fascinating to watch. It's amazing to see this type of work taking place on your doorstep."

Howdon resident Alan Devine worked for Bouygues TP on the South Cut-and-Cover section. He joined the team in early February 2009 as a Chartered Civil Engineer. He enjoyed the challenges a project of that scale threw up on a daily basis. Recalling the enormous sense of satisfaction associated with construction on such a large scale, he explained "Being involved with such a dedicated and skilled team of people ensures continual professional growth as an engineer".

The majority of specialist consultants and sub-contractors appointed by Bouygues Travaux Publics were also locally based. A dedicated local supplier database was established to assist Bouygues project staff in identifying potential local sub-contractors and suppliers. This supplemented a CV database of all those interested in applying for opportunities on site.

"We visited Bouygues at a Meet the Buyer event and showed them the type of work we've done to date, and the quality standards we work towards. We were pleased to be asked to quote to supply pipework for the project – and even happier to have won the work! Not only does this contract help sustain our business through a global recession, safeguarding jobs for our staff, but it also gives us a chance to be involved in a project of international significance, which is fantastic for our reputation and business profile." South Shields engineering firm.

"We work throughout the region and have been involved in some interesting jobs in the past, but it's great to be able to play a part in such a major scheme so close to home. There's a slow down in growth throughout the construction industry, so this project is appreciated even more in the current economic climate." Wallsend contracting firm.

A community project

THE route of the second Vehicle Tunnel runs beneath central Jarrow. During construction this meant that one of the largest housing areas in the town was largely cut off from the main shopping and administrative area. North of the Tyne, the construction route ran to the west of East Howdon, arguably isolating an already secluded urban village. Recognising the potential difficulties that might arise during construction TWITA placed great importance on community engagement during the works. TT2 demonstrated its commitment to community partnering during the bidding process and upon appointment Newcastle-based wood holmes led a team of community liaison and stakeholder partnering officers, whose focus was on local community issues.

Partnering forums were set up on both sides of the Tyne, bringing together representatives from the local communities, including residents, Ward Councillors, businesses, and voluntary groups. The forums were intended to provide a structured and open opportunity for people to find out about and question site activities. In addition to the community-based forums, a strategic partnering forum was also established. This involved representatives of key regional bodies such as the Highways and Environment Agency, as well as members of the local partnering forums. The forums helped to ensure that the delivery of the construction works was carefully and sensitively managed.

Drop-in sessions were held three times a week, every week during the peak of construction works. During the refurbishment phase of activities this dropped to twice weekly sessions, one each side of the river. The regular drop-in sessions helped members of the local communities to chat about the project in an informal setting.

Hundreds of site tours and presentations were delivered during the lifetime of the New Tyne Crossing project. The nature of a road tunnel project is that the construction works tend to be hidden away out of sight. Hence offering site tours for interested people enabled a wider audience to share the experience. For safety reasons, the school tours were limited to the perimeter of the construction site, with special viewing points installed along the site fence line to provide a window onto the activities within. However, a group of students from Jarrow School were permitted to break the boundaries of the site, equipped with suitable protective clothing and a full safety briefing. Under the tutelage of their teacher, Mr McGregor, they established a film group that would document the building of the new Tyne Tunnel. Their research was educational and the end product, screened at the Royal opening of the New Tyne Crossing, was intended to inform those who watched it.

TYNE TUNNEL
MAINTENANCE
BOUYGUES
TRAVAUX PUBLICS
UK Branch

BOUYGUES
TRAVAUX PUBLICS
UK Branch
BOUYGUES
TRAVAUX PUBLICS
UK Branch
BOUYGUES
TRAVAUX PUBLICS
UK Branch

Keeping traffic flowing

THE fundamental reason for the New Tyne Crossing was to improve the way that traffic flowed across the Tyne. This desire to keep the road network flowing freely was extended through to construction. One of the main project objectives was to minimise impacts on traffic at the fourth worst bottleneck in the country, while the construction of the new Vehicle Tunnel and approach roads was carried out. This was no mean feat!

TT2 traffic officers were instrumental in keeping the site working as efficiently as possible. TT2's Managing Director during construction was Trevor Jackson. He recalls "Traffic flows like water – it will always seek the route of least resistance. This is why motorists are quick to find the 'rat runs' around traffic jams. It was this behaviour that caused us challenges at the south junction, with people trying to shortcut the A19 queues via the hamburger roundabout.

"The other behaviour I noticed at the tunnel approach was the way motorists danced around one another rather than slotting neatly from multiple lanes into single file. This created significant delays."

Before construction works had even begun, Trevor introduced changes to the traffic lane alignments. These changes also helped motorists to grow accustomed to the rows of traffic cones that would become so commonplace during the works. With cones in place, motorists were forced to merge into single file in a more structured and orderly manner. This had an instant and notable impact on traffic flow, freeing up movement considerably. Ongoing tweaks to lane alignments and merges throughout the works enabled journey times to be kept to a minimum despite building works taking place directly adjacent to the stream of live traffic.

Keeping an eye on the queues

TWITA realised that it would be important to provide motorists with reliable information about journey times during construction. For many years prior to construction traffic and travel news bulletins were based on estimates regarding the queues at the Tyne Tunnel. It was TWITA's concern that these guess-based estimates were not always very accurate, and yet they could influence public perceptions about the delays. TWITA committed to invest in technology that would provide a more reliable indication in order to remove the guess work, and help people to make informed decisions about which route to take.

Journey time monitoring equipment was installed before construction began, so that people had a baseline to compare journey times to. It meant that any construction-related delays would be clearly flagged up. The technology works by recording vehicle registration plates on the approach to the tunnel, and measuring the time taken for a vehicle to travel from one camera point to the far side of the river. Fortunately the technology revealed that for the majority of the time journey times were the same, if not better, than they had been prior to building works.

The journey time data via the TT2 website, along with the tunnel web cams, became invaluable to many motorists in planning their cross-river journeys. It was important for TWITA that people were not unnecessarily deterred from using the Tyne Tunnel during construction, not only for reasons of customer service but because of the extra load this would place on other parts of the road network. In fact, customer numbers remained strong at the Tyne Tunnel throughout the project.

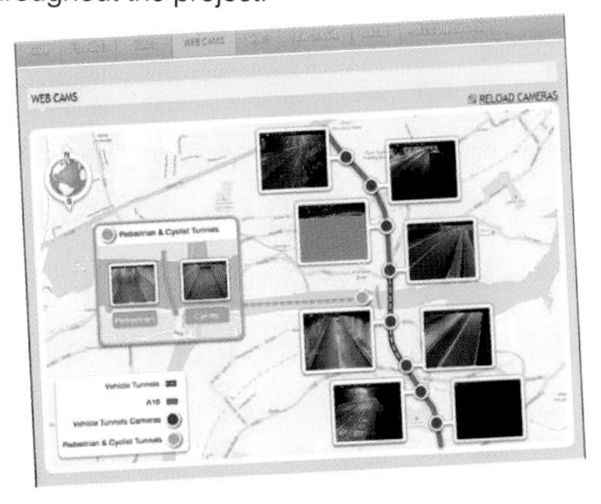

Stitching the land together again

THE construction of the new Vehicle Tunnel required a swathe of land through Jarrow and Howdon to be cleared. A 30m deep trench was cut through the landscape, and once re-filled it was important that an improved version was returned for public enjoyment. It had already been agreed with the planning authorities of North and South Tyneside Councils that all trees cleared to make way for the new tunnel should be replaced with native alternatives. Many of the trees that were felled before construction began had been overgrown 'weeds' and imported species. Under the landscaping master plan, each tree that was removed was replaced with an equivalent that would be indigenous to the local habitat, in other words species of tree that belong in the environment in which they grow.

In addition to this agreement, it was important to determine where these plants would appear on the new landscape. Hence a major public consultation exercise was launched to find out how local communities and special interest groups would like to see the landscape developed. A wide range of consultation activities took place to tease out public views, including a pizza and poster session with local youth groups. Key themes emerging were that people preferred the idea of smaller, less dense plantings rather than tall, thick wooded areas that might provide a hiding place for those with criminal intent. A linear shared footpath and cycleway was seen as an attractive feature of the new parkland through Jarrow, with one large, mixed age play area rather than separate ones.

An interesting aspect of discussion related to the redevelopment of the Riverside Park. One of the suggestions put forward was that an amphitheatre might provide an unusual forum for entertainment down by the Tyne. However the vast majority of local people considered this idea to be unrealistic. A suggestion for a play area for teenagers was put forward by numerous different groups and individuals, with suggestions ranging from a skate park to a cycle track. It was ultimately agreed that the community inspired idea of a youth-orientated skate park should be developed.

Dedicated consultation events had been held in local schools. Hence it was fitting that the first tree in Jarrow was planted by school children from Dunn Street Primary School, with Councillor Tom Hanson.

On the north side of the river, the first of thousands of trees to be replanted was placed in the ground by members of the local partnering forums, Linda Whitworth, of East Howdon Community Association, and Mary Finnegan, of Jarrow.

TT2
Landscape Masterplan - North

A cultured crossing

THE legacy of the New Tyne Crossing was not only the gift of an engineering project that transformed the daily lives of thousands of motorists. More than that, the project delivered a range of cultural activities that engaged and entertained audiences during the delivery of the scheme.

Foreign Exchange

Visits from several twin town delegations, linked with North and South Tyneside, were hosted on site during construction. In order to maximise the interest for foreign visitors bi-lingual tours were delivered with specially prepared handouts for guests. At-a-glance guides to the construction works were produced in both German and French, and proved extremely popular with visitors.

Sketch & Safety

It was important that school children living near the construction site understood the risks associated with building sites, and were actively discouraged from trying to sneak onto the site. To tackle this challenge a series of safety art competitions were run during the course of the project to both educate local children and to produce posters that could be displayed around the site hoardings.

Each year that the competition took place it was encouraging to note the increase in knowledge amongst the school children, about construction site health and safety. The standards grew, and the variety of posters expanded. It proved increasingly challenging to select the winning efforts. However luckily a few stars shone out amongst the wealth of good quality entries, and these winning designs were transformed into site signage and displayed around the site perimeter as an illustrated warning for those contemplating entering the building site.

Tile and tile again...

During the refurbishment of the original Vehicle Tunnel a stockpile of the mosaic tiles that had lined the tunnel's interior was discovered. The redesign of the tunnel meant that these tiles were no longer required, hence new uses for the old tiles were sought.

Boxes of the original tunnel tiles were donated to a variety of good causes, including local primary school, Stephenson Memorial School, and East Howdon community centre, for use in specific projects. A nearby sports club also used some of the tiles to redecorate its changing rooms.

Willington Quay artist, Anne Heraghty, created a dazzling piece of mirrored art with the box of tiles she was given. She decided to donate the artwork to tunnel operator, TT2 Limited, where the piece is currently displayed.

From windscreen to silver screen

In association with the Tunnel 2K race promoter, David Burdus, TT2 hosted a mini film festival in April 2010. Held at the Tyneside Cinema in Newcastle, the festival showcased three short films celebrating human achievement in the face of great challenge on Tyneside. This included rare footage of the construction of the first Vehicle Tunnel, and a forgotten film created by students from King's College, Durham (now Newcastle University) in 1953 to raise funds during the university's rag week for the Percy Hedley Foundation.

The main feature at the film festival was a short yet powerful piece capturing the drama and intensity of the Tunnel2K wheelchair race. "T2K 2009 – The Percy Hedley Edit" was created by service users at Percy Hedley Foundation Karten Media Suite. The film packs a particular punch with its soundtrack, which Charlie Harcourt, former member of the band Lindisfarne, helped to compose. The music was created by project workers using sound beam technology, which enables music to be created by cutting an invisible beam using hands or even eyelids.

Arty artefacts

A £10,000 initiative delivered in partnership with North Tyneside Council sought to create an eye catching welcome for motorists arriving through the northbound tunnel . Three refurbished marine buoys were transformed by Jarrow artist Linda Nelson. The buoys took several months to undergo their treatment, and can be seen today on arrival via the Tyne Tunnel in North Tyneside featuring their '1950s railway poster' inspired designs. Each buoy captures a local landmark or special attraction.

A fresh look at the past

In partnership with South Tyneside charities Find Your Talent and Bede's World, the organisations behind the New Tyne Crossing project delivered an art project with dramatic outputs.

Design elements were developed with groups of young people at Bede's World, drawing upon inspiration from local author Tom Kelly. Internationally renowned urban art collectives Newline and Heavy Artillery worked with the groups to create storyboards, and finally to translate the designs through graffiti artworks onto the site hoardings of the construction site in Jarrow.

The art panels told the story of some of Jarrow's key historical milestones, including the work of the Venerable Bede and the efforts of the Jarrow March. The contemporary artwork became a leisure attraction in its own right, transforming the functional site fencing into an urban art gallery.

Push bar to open

Wheeling through the night

AT the time of going to print the Tyne Tunnels had played host to twelve elite wheelchair races. The races attract the very best wheelchair athletes in the world, and tend to take place late at night, after the peak traffic flow has passed. The annual race, known as the Tunnel 2K, has gained cult status amongst the wheelchair racing fraternity, and is the only event the Vehicle Tunnels are closed for. The race is always held in the northbound tunnel, other than in 2011 when the tunnel was closed for refurbishment, and the course took athletes through the newly commissioned southbound tunnel instead.

The thrilling race features a fast paced downhill section, during which athletes can reach speeds of 50mph. From mid-river the course covers a long, steep climb back out to the river bank north of the Tyne. The lung busting climb has been described by gold medal winning Paralympian, David Weir, as so tough that he could taste blood in his mouth. Definitely not for the faint hearted!

The race has attracted an incredible field of athletes during its twelve years, including Baroness Tanni Grey Thompson, who has attended every event, and took part in the first six races.

London 2012 gold medal winner Mickey Bushell is a keen supporter of Tunnel 2K, having participated in the race since he was a young teenager. Canadian marathon World Record holder, Josh Cassidy, has a hatrick of Tunnel 2K wins under his belt. The professional athlete is also a commercial illustrator, and produced a stunning piece of art to celebrate this unique race.

"There is nothing like Tunnel 2K on the planet" Baroness Grey Thompson

9
8

BOUYGUES
UK Branch
burdus
INTERNATIONAL 2009
burdus
NAPPER

TUNNEL 2K
INTERNATIONAL
RACE
promoted by burdus
TT2

TYNE AND WEAR
INTEGRATED TRANSPORT AUTHORITY

TT2

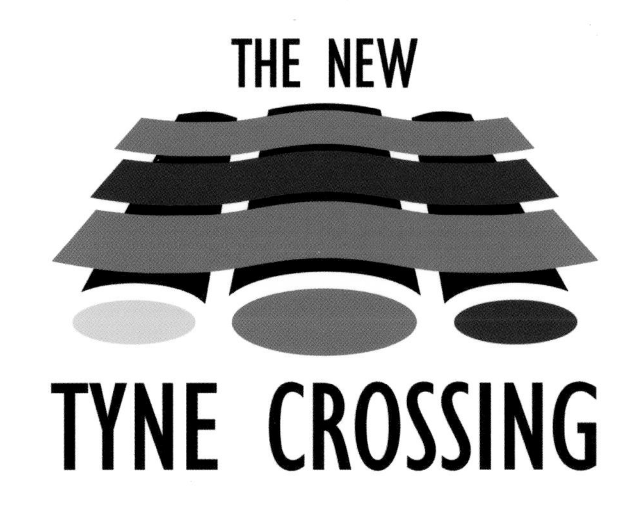
THE NEW
TYNE CROSSING

BOUYGUES
TRAVAUX PUBLICS

PARSONS BRINCKERHOFF

Key Designer - Approvals, Environmental Compliance, Civil/Structural Design

Manufacture, Flotation & Submersion of River Units

ARUP

Technical Advisor to scheme Promoter, TWITA

Specialist Geotechnical Contractor Diaphragm Walls & Piling

Temporary Traffic Management and Lining

SCADA & Data Communications Integration Specialist

Strategic Communications & Stakeholder Partnering Specialist

CAPITA SYMONDS

The faces behind the project

Paul Fenwick, Project Director, TWITA

Paul Fenwick is the New Tyne Crossing Project Director on behalf of the project's promoter, the Tyne & Wear Integrated Transport Authority (TWITA).

Paul has had an instrumental role in the project during his 14 year involvement. Throughout the process he has never failed in trying to ensure the social, economic and environmental objectives of the scheme were met.

He was first involved with the project in 1998 when he presented a report to the TWITA for approval of a new vehicle crossing of the Tyne to help alleviate traffic congestion. He worked on all aspects of the project, and retains an incredibly detailed knowledge of the scheme. From the outset he developed close working relationships with the riparian councils of North Tyneside and South Tyneside, as well as establishing links with community groups in the areas that would be affected by the proposed works.

His personal commitment to the project, and his determination to seek fair outcomes to the various issues arising, has won him respect amongst a wide range of stakeholders, even during the challenging and difficult times a project of this scale can encounter.

"I never imagined that I would spend this long working on the scheme, but I must admit that it has been a fascinating and enjoyable experience. To have faced the variety and scale of challenges we've seen on this scheme, and eventually to have witnessed the successful outcomes, makes the hard work worthwhile."

Councillor Muriel Green,
Chair of the Tyne Tunnels Working Group

Muriel Green was a North Tyneside Councillor appointed to the TWITA Tyne Tunnels Working Group during in 1999. During the preparation of the documents for the Tyne Tunnels Order, Cllr. Green was the Chair of the Working Group and, along with Cllr. Tom Hanson from South Tyneside Council, she was responsible for the submission of the Order.

Cllr. Green was actively involved in promoting the project during its earliest phases, encouraging the wider public to recognise the tremendous need and potential benefits of the scheme. She was part of the TWITA group that initiated the procurement process for the Concessionaire in 2004, and even after leaving TWITA she retained an avid interest in the project.

"Having been so heavily involved in promoting the New Tyne Crossing scheme in the early days, and supporting it through Public Inquiry, I watched the construction progress from afar with very great interest and excited anticipation. On the day that both tunnels came into use I felt incredibly proud of what had been achieved."

Councillor Tom Hanson,
Chair of the Tyne Tunnels Working Group

South Tyneside Councillor Tom Hanson represented Bede Ward for 20 years, until 2012, during which time he saw the development of the proposal, the Public Inquiry, and the eventual delivery of the New Tyne Crossing project works. As Vice-Chair of TWITA, and Chair of the Tyne Tunnels Working Group during delivery of the works, Cllr. Hanson was determined to do all that he could to minimise disruption for the people of Jarrow. Once works had started through Central Jarrow, Cllr. Hanson dedicated time every week to walking the site perimeter to look for any issues of potential concern for local people. He requested weekly project briefings from the construction team and never veered away from challenging the issues he felt were most important for the people of Jarrow.

"I am delighted to see both tunnels fully operational. The nature of the construction works caused unavoidable disruption. However the construction and refurbishment were carried out with great care and consideration for the people of Jarrow. Local people have been extremely understanding and I give my heartfelt thanks for their patience."

Tom Hanson sadly passed away in October 2012, after a short illness.

Trevor Jackson,
Managing Director,
TT2

Trevor Jackson left a previous project in Jamaica to move to the UK in 2007, in the role of TT2's Managing Director. With a great deal of experience in similar toll road construction projects around the world, he was quickly able to identify improvements to the traffic management procedures in place at the Tyne Tunnel, that would prove invaluable in minimising disruption during construction.

Trevor was also quick to identify the potential traffic issues that would arise on completion of the scheme, if no intervening improvements were made to the Silverlink (A1058) junction 3 miles north of the tunnel. He urged local politicians and business leaders to address the existing traffic congestion problems at Silverlink so that by the time both Tyne Tunnels were in operation the junction had undergone interim road widening works, and the A19 flowed better than ever.

Throughout the project Trevor made it his mission to have an open door policy, welcoming meetings with motorists, local residents, and businesses where issues of concern existed. He became the face of the project and helped to push it to completion earlier than planned, for the benefit of motorists and the wider region.

"This has been an unbelievable project. People told us they didn't believe we could improve journey times during construction. They didn't believe we could take the communities with us on the journey. They couldn't believe there would be no queues once both tunnels were open. But by the end of the project, people told us what we'd achieved was unbelievable."

TOMMY TYNE TUNNEL AND HIS TERRIFIC

THE TYNE TUNNELS